MW00630129

Luminaries

Profiles of Women in Academic Medicine

Jaclyn L. Kovach, M.D.

Luminaries: Profiles of Women in Academic Medicine
By Jaclyn L. Kovach, MD

Library of Congress Control Number: 2020903880
ISBN 978-1-7345837-0-0

Cover art and book design by Kim A. Foster Graphic Design
Edited by Alexandra Bassil

I would like to thank everyone at the
University of Miami Miller School of Medicine
for their support including
Dr. Rose Van Zuilen, Associate Editor, and the
Women in Academic Medicine organization;
Janet Bringuez-Sanchez and the Office of
Diversity; and Dr. Edward Abraham,
Executive Vice President for Health Affairs,
Dr. Julio Frenk, President, and
Professor Felicia Marie Knaul.
Also, I am very grateful to our primary donor,
Mr. James F. Blinder,
for making this book a reality.

– J.L.K.

Preface by Jaclyn L. Kovach, MD

When I was 6 years old, I had trouble falling asleep at night. I would lay in bed for hours with my mind racing – thinking about pressing issues like games we would play during recess the next day, doing math problems in my head, and wondering when sleep would come. My parents thought listening to books on tape would lull me to sleep so they gave me biographical audio cassettes featuring women like Harriet Tubman, Deborah Sampson Gannett, Mary Cassatt, and Elizabeth Blackwell.

I am not sure if my parents could have predicted the impact these biographies would have on me. I internalized the trials and tribulations they overcame and can recall many passages to this day. Not only were these accounts each unique but they were incredibly inspiring. As a young woman when I was faced with a challenge I often thought to myself, "If they can accomplish great achievements against the odds, then why can't I?"

I grew up in Pittsburgh, Pennsylvania and there were no doctors in my family. My great-grandparents immigrated from Europe and my grandfathers were both coal miners. My paternal grandfather, a World War II veteran and fervent believer in higher education, saved every penny so that my father and uncle could earn engineering degrees. (He attended my medical school graduation at the age of 87 and was overjoyed!)

My parents encouraged my academic pursuits and made many sacrifices for my education. When I decided I wanted to apply to medical school, my friend's father, an academic neurologist, provided indispensable counsel. This was my first exposure to the spirit of mentorship that is the foundation of medical education.

Twenty years later, in the middle stage of my career, I have developed an even greater appreciation for mentorship – the selfless facilitation of another's career. Such guidance is both necessary and potentially life-changing but securing it can be elusive.

A career in science is challenging by nature and that is part of the allure. With a myriad of potential career paths to take and continuously evolving niches to be filled, during training it is impossible to have direct exposure to all of them. Mentors can help young colleagues navigate this daunting academic landscape. Beyond establishing a satisfying and productive career path, a mentor can advise how to avoid and recover from time-consuming pitfalls which we all encounter. There are other broader challenges that arise during career development. Some may include deciding whether to have children, cultivating a support system (none of my accomplishments would be possible without the support of my husband), and most importantly preserving your well-being so you can help others to the best of your ability and enjoy your life.

My desire to offer mentorship, guidance, and inspiration was the driving force behind the creation of this book. I hope while becoming immersed in the powerful stories of your incredible contemporaries and colleagues you find the key to achieving your personal definition of success. It is not magic or a secret recipe, but rather unwavering resolve, thoughtful decision-making, a strong support system, and subscribing to the notion of "They're doing it, why can't I?" ∎

Foreword by Dean Henri R. Ford, MD, MHA

This impressive collection of essays written by women faculty at the University of Miami Leonard M. Miller School of Medicine should be read by both young women and men who aspire to study medicine. These essays recount the hopes and dreams of these amazing trailblazers as well as the sacrifices they had to make and adversities they had to overcome to achieve their goals. They reflect their passion, their commitment to the relentless pursuit of excellence, and their tenacity or resilience. These essays are a source of inspiration for everyone in academia, regardless of one's profession or specialty. They remind us of the great strides that women in academic medicine have made through sheer grit and determination, and the obstacles that must be overcome to achieve gender equity in medicine.

The number of women graduating from medical schools and from biomedical doctoral degree programs continues to increase. The tales of courage and conviction that abound in these essays remind us that we already have the right substrate for current and future leaders in academic medicine. Therefore, it is imperative that our profession creates more opportunities for women to assume leadership positions in academic medicine. These women are exemplary role models for students, residents, and junior faculty, regardless of gender. ■

TABLE OF CONTENTS

Preface by
Jaclyn L. Kovach, MD   2

Foreword by
Dean Henri R. Ford, MD, MHA   3

Margaret A. Pericak-Vance, PhD   11

Kassandra M. Bosire, MD   17

G. Patricia Cantwell, MD   21

Gillian Ann Hotz, PhD   27

Audina Berrocal, MD   33

Kimberly L. Reynolds, MD   37

Yiliam Rodriguez-Blanco, MD   45

Joan E. St. Onge, MD, MPH, FACP   49

Sheila Ann Conway, MD, FAOA   55

Janet L. Davis, MD, MA   61

Elizabeth J. Franzmann, MD   65

Lilian M. Abbo, MD, FIDSA   71

Viviana Elizabeth Horigian, MD, MHA   75

Stefanie Brown, MD, FACP, FAAP   81

Omaida C. Velazquez, MD   87

Ana E. Campo, MD   93

Elizabeth A. Crocco, MD   97

Mary Bartlett Bunge, PhD   103

Gauri Agarwal, MD, FACP   109

Ellen Faye Barrett, PhD   115

Monica M. Yepes, MD   121

Marie Denise Gervais, MD   127

JoNell Efantis Potter, PhD, APRN, FAAN   131

Teshamae Monteith, MD   135

Epilogue by
Congresswoman Donna Shalala   141

Jaclyn L. Kovach, MD
Associate Professor of Clinical Ophthalmology
Fellowship Director
Bascom Palmer Eye Institute
University of Miami Miller School of Medicine

Dean Henri R. Ford, MD, MHA
Dean and Chief Academic Officer
University of Miami Miller School of Medicine

Margaret A. Pericak-Vance, PhD
Director, John P. Hussman Institute for
Human Genomics
Dr. John T. Macdonald Foundation
Professor of Human Genetics
Executive Vice Chair, Dr. John T. Macdonald
Foundation Department of Human Genetics
John P. Hussman Institute for Human Genomics
University of Miami Miller School of Medicine

Kassandra M. Bosire, MD
Assistant Clinical Professor
Residency Program Director
Department of Family Medicine and
Community Health
University of Miami Miller School of Medicine

G. Patricia Cantwell, MD

Chief, Division of Pediatric Critical Care
Medicine
Director, Pediatric Palliative Medicine
Medical Manager,
US&R South Florida Task Force 2
University of Miami Miller School
of Medicine

21

Yiliam Rodriguez-Blanco, MD

Professor, Clinical Anesthesiology
Chief of Cardiothoracic Anesthesia
& Associate Vice Chair for Clinical
Research
Department of Anesthesiology/
Division of Cardiac Anesthesia
University of Miami Miller School
of Medicine

45

Gillian Ann Hotz, PhD

Director KiDZ Neuroscience Center
Director Concussion Program
Director WalkSafe, BikeSafe and
SkateSafe Programs
Research Professor
Department of Neurosurgery
The Miami Project to Cure
Paralysis
University of Miami Miller School
of Medicine

27

Joan E. St. Onge, MD, MPH, FACP

Associate Professor of Clinical
Medicine
Senior Associate Dean for Faculty
Affairs
Interim Chair, Department of
Medical Education
University of Miami Miller School
of Medicine

49

Audina Berrocal, MD

Professor of Clinical
Ophthalmology
Medical Director of Pediatric
Retinal and ROP
Vitreoretinal Fellowship Director
Bascom Palmer Eye Institute
University of Miami Miller School
of Medicine

33

Sheila Ann Conway, MD, FAOA

Professor & Chief, Division of
Orthopedic Oncology
Program Director
Orthopedic Surgery Residency &
Musculoskeletal Oncology
Fellowship Programs
Department of Orthopedic Surgery
University of Miami Miller School
of Medicine

55

Kimberly L. Reynolds, MD

Assistant Professor of Clinical
Pediatrics
University of Miami Miller School
of Medicine
Pediatric Hospitalist
Holtz Children's Hospital at
Jackson Memorial Medical Center

37

Janet L. Davis, MD, MA

Leach Distinguished Professor
of Ophthalmology
Bascom Palmer Eye Institute
University of Miami Miller School
of Medicine

61

Elizabeth J. Franzmann, MD

Associate Professor
Department of Otolaryngology
University of Miami Miller School
of Medicine

65

Omaida C. Velazquez, MD

Professor and Chair, DeWitt Daughtry
Family Department of Surgery
David Kimmelman Endowed Chair in
Vascular Surgery
Surgeon-in-Chief for UMHC/UHealth
System & Jackson Health System
University of Miami Miller School
of Medicine

87

Lilian M. Abbo, MD, FIDSA

Chief Infection Prevention &
Antimicrobial Stewardship
Jackson Health System
Professor of Infectious Diseases
Department of Medicine &
Miami Transplant Institute
University of Miami Miller School
of Medicine

71

Ana E. Campo, MD

Professor of Clinical Psychiatry
Associate Dean for Student Affairs
Director For Medical Student
Education in Psychiatry
University of Miami Miller School
of Medicine

93

Viviana E. Horigian, MD, MHA

Associate Professor
Director of Public Health Education
University of Miami Miller School
of Medicine

75

Elizabeth A. Crocco, MD

Medical Director
UM Memory Disorder Clinic
Center for Cognitive Neuroscience & Aging
Chief, Division of Geriatric Psychiatry
Associate Clinical Professor
Department of Psychiatry and Behavioral
Sciences
University of Miami Miller School
of Medicine
Geriatric Psychiatry Training Director
Jackson Memorial Hospital

97

Stefanie Brown, MD, FACP, FAAP

Program Director
Internal Medicine
Section Chief – Med-Peds
Section Chief – Pediatric Hospital
Medicine
Assistant Professor of Medicine
and Pediatrics
University of Miami Miller School
of Medicine

81

Mary Bartlett Bunge, PhD

Former Christine E. Lynn Distinguished
Professor of Neuroscience
Professor Emerita of Cell Biology, Neurolog-
ical Surgery and Neurology
Doctor of Humane Science
honoris causa
University of Miami Miller School
of Medicine

103

Gauri Agarwal, MD, FACP

Associate Dean for Clinical Curriculum
University of Miami Miller School
of Medicine

109

JoNell Efantis Potter, PhD, APRN, FAAN

Professor of Clinical Obstetrics,
Gynecology & Reproductive Sciences
Vice Chair, Reproductive Sciences
Chief, Women's HIV Service
Director, THRIVE Clinic
University of Miami Miller School
of Medicine

131

Ellen Faye Barrett, PhD

Professor of Physiology &
Biophysics
University of Miami Miller School
of Medicine

115

Teshamae Monteith, MD

Chief, Headache Division
Fellowship Program Director
Associate Professor of
Clinical Neurology
Department of Neurology
University of Miam Miller School
of Medicine

135

Monica M. Yepes, MD

Associate Professor of Radiology
Chief, Breast Imaging
Director of Breast Imaging Services
University of Miami Miller School
of Medicine

121

Congresswoman Donna E. Shalala

141

Marie Denise Gervais, MD

Assistant Dean for Admissions and
Diversity
Director, Pre-Doctoral Education
Department of Family Medicine and
Community Health
University of Miami Miller School
of Medicine

127

Dedicated to our understanding
and supportive families and friends.
Without your love and encouragement,
we could not live our dreams.

Margaret A. Pericak-Vance, PhD

Director, John P. Hussman Institute for Human Genomics
Dr. John T. Macdonald Foundation
Professor of Human Genetics
Executive Vice Chair, Dr. John T. Macdonald Foundation
Department of Human Genetics
John P. Hussman Institute for Human Genomics
University of Miami Miller School of Medicine

My goal is to leave an indelible mark on human genetics research.

I often recall the anonymous inspirational quote, "If my strength intimidates you, I hope you realize that's a weakness of yours." By dedicating my life to scientific discovery, I've identified genes that contribute to or protect against a range of human diseases while enjoying a fascinating and extraordinary career.

My sustained contributions to human genetics and genomics began during the peak of the human genome project and include discovering genetic risk and protective factors for conditions such as Alzheimer disease (AD), autism, age-related macular degeneration (AMD), and multiple sclerosis (MS).

Throughout my career, I made strides to advance our understanding of the complex relationships between genes and health. My hard work led me to establish important milestones in more than 30 human diseases, including neurological, psychiatric, and ophthalmological diseases. I have produced – at last count – more than 700 refereed journal articles, 30 book chapters, and other scholarly publications, which have been cited 116,164 times in the scientific literature and earned an h-index of 137.

When I was a young woman, my father told me in no uncertain terms that pursuing higher-level education was something he expected me to do. He instilled in me to believe I could do or be anything I wanted. There were no double standards in my home regarding gender, and that gave me confidence to pursue my dreams.

I began studying science at Wells College in Aurora, New York, where I attained my bachelor's degree in biology in 1973. I earned my PhD in medical genetics at Indiana University (IU) Medical Center in 1978 under Dr. PM Conneally, one of the leaders in the field. It was in the graduate program at IU where I met my husband of 43 years, Jeffery M. Vance, MD, PhD. To this day, we are partners in research and life. I bring the genetic epidemiology expertise and his forte is molecular biology. Jeff, a highly successful researcher and physician, has always supported my career.

I pursued postdoctoral training in statistical genetics and genetic epidemiology at the University of North Carolina at Chapel Hill under Dr. Robert Elston, one of the icons in the field. From there, I went to Duke University Medical Center in Durham, North Carolina, where I rose through the ranks. In 1981, I began working as a research associate in the division of neurology. By 1999, I was a James B. Duke Professor of Medicine and Director of the Duke Center for Human Genetics and the first PhD tenured professor in the department of medicine.

From 1981-2006, I thrived at Duke and discovered most of the late-onset AD risk is due to a common variant, the E4 allele of apolipoprotein E (*APOE*) gene. The article (Corder et al, *Science*, 1993) is still the most frequently cited paper in AD biomedical research. My collaborators and I showed the risk of developing AD was eight times higher in people with two copies of *APOE4* than in people with the lowest "gene dose" (zero copies). That's an incredibly robust connection, and our research team was surprised the effect was so strong. Geneticist John Hardy called the discovery of a link between the *APOE4* gene and AD "the most important finding that's ever been made in the epidemiology of Alzheimer's disease." Although the paper was published over 25 years ago, it still receives hundreds of citations annually *(e.g. 409 citations in 2018, according to Google Scholar)*.

At Duke my group was also the first to identify the E2 allele of the *APOE* gene protects against AD (Corder et al, *Nature Genetics*, 1994). A few years later, my collaborators and I discovered a common coding polymorphism in the *CFH* gene greatly increases the risk of developing AMD. This discovery follows only my *APOE4* study in terms of critical importance to the field of human genetics, as it confirmed the role of inflammation in the development of AMD (Haines et al, *Science*, 2005). The director of the National Institutes of Health (NIH) at the time, Dr. Elias Zherhouni, described this discovery as one of the NIH's most important breakthroughs of 2005. My laboratory also identified a variant of Interleukin 7 receptor alpha chain (*ILR7*) as a risk factor for MS (Gregory et al, *Nature Genetics*, 2007). NIH recognized the MS genetics discovery as the most significant MS genetics breakthrough since the 1970s.

However, my professional success at Duke did not protect me from personal loss. On December 12, 1998, tragedy struck when our son, Jeffery Joseph "JJ" Vance, a kind, intelligent, athletic 14-year-old with his whole life in front of him, died suddenly from a rare clotting disorder (thrombotic storm) after incurring a minor knee injury while playing soccer. Jeff and I were devastated, as was our daughter, Danica. To honor his memory, we formed the JJ Vance Foundation and established a scholarship and summer internship program for well-deserving seniors at East Chapel Hill High School, the school JJ attended in Chapel Hill, North Carolina.

In 2007, I transitioned to the University Miami (UM) to become Director of the John P. Hussman Institute for Human Genomics (HIHG), and the JJ Vance Summer Internship continues here, drawing applicants from across South Florida.

Shortly after JJ's death, Danica introduced her father and I to an 8th grader named Richard Belton. Eventually, Jeff and I became his legal guardians and Richard became and remains today a member of our family. Richard was accepted at prestigious Wake Forest University (WFU) in NC and was awarded a football scholarship. He played for WFU culminating in an Atlantic Coast Conference Championship and Orange Bowl appearance. We were so proud when he graduated from WFU with a degree in history. He is now a successful South Florida-based basketball coach and youth leader. Richard grew up never knowing his father. As part of our "genetically-oriented family" he analyzed his DNA with a 23andMe test kit and discovered in addition to African heritage, he is also Scandinavian, mainly Swedish in origin. Richard opened our eyes to the importance of diversity in genomics research. When he joined our family, I grew increasingly aware of the impact genomics research study design can have on health disparities of diverse populations, specifically race and ethnicity. I wanted my research to be more inclusive, to narrow existing health disparities and contribute to the development of treatments that benefit everyone.

We also expanded the goals of the JJ Vance foundation. From 2000-2006, we awarded scholarships to top-performing seniors at East Chapel Hill and Chapel Hill High Schools. Our program evolved into the JJ Vance Memorial Summer Internship in Biological and Computational Sciences (JJ Vance Internship), which, while open to all students, targets young people who otherwise would not have the opportunity to explore research in STEM (science, technology, engineering, and math) during high school. Programs that offer formal scientific mentorship and access to hands-on learning in STEM are limited at many underfunded high schools. The JJ Vance Internship engages juniors (rising seniors) in an exciting and challenging, eight-week research course. The interns are welcomed onto teams conducting ongoing research projects and given the chance to work directly with graduate students and postdoctoral fellows. By experiencing research first-hand, the interns learn about the opportunities available to them while developing creativity, learning about the intellectual rewards of scientific research, and gaining the confidence needed to be successful in a variety of fields. I am grateful my husband and I, along with our many family members and friends, honor JJ's memory by providing this amazing opportunity to underserved, smart, science-loving high school students.

The HIHG's mission is to use the very latest technology to identify genes involved in human diseases for diagnosis, intervention, and prevention of illness. Our work ranges across many scientific disciplines and involves close collaboration with the global community of scientists and medical professionals, and the community.

With nearly 30 HIHG faculty members of which more than 40% are women, they serve in academic appointments in many different departments, including the Dr. John T. Macdonald Foundation Department of Human Genetics (DHG), pediatrics, medicine, and neurology. Additionally, dozens of other top-tier scientists from numerous schools, departments, and institutes are HIHG associate members. We employ some of the world's top geneticists, a fact that is evidenced by our continued high levels of NIH funding.

Alzheimer disease is *the* flagship research area at the HIHG, and one of my main research targets. Our efforts to identify the genes that contribute to (and protect against) all forms of dementia are world-renowned. To facilitate the development of new treatments for AD by 2022, I lead several large consortium efforts, including the Alzheimer's Disease Sequencing Project (ADSP) Follow-up Study (FUS) with its unprecedented effort to generate whole genome sequence data for more than 40,000 individuals over the next five years.

To date most clinical research has been conducted on people who are white, non-Hispanic, and, until recently, male. The astounding lack of diversity in the populations recruited for genomic studies has real-life consequences.

Partly as a result of Richard joining our family, I realized how critical it was to change this paradigm and include all populations in medical research. When new treatments are developed using primarily or exclusively data gathered from non-Hispanic whites, the resulting therapies are, unavoidably, tailored to benefit this specific population subset. At best, careless study design is delaying the ability of some populations to benefit from precision/personalized medicine. At worst, overt discrimination is depriving those most at risk for certain health conditions from receiving the treatments they desperately need.

In 40 years, a staggering 13.9 million people in the Unites States will be diagnosed with Alzheimer disease – nearly triple today's prevalence of about 5 million Americans – according to a recent study by researchers at the Centers for Disease Control and Prevention (CDC). African Americans and Hispanic Americans will be hardest hit. Those are precisely the populations least represented in biomedical research.

Rosalind Franklin, the female scientist who set the stage for Watson and Crick to discover that DNA forms a double helix, once said, "Science and everyday life cannot and should not be separated," and I agree the two are linked forever. Recruitment for biomedical research is certainly a scientific area with tangible real-world effects.

That's why much of my current research is dedicated to addressing health disparities in genomics research. I strongly believe that everyone, regardless of race, class, or gender, should have access to precision/personalized medicine. I am convinced by studying ethnically diverse genomes, discovery of protective variants for numerous diseases can be utilized for targeted drug therapies to benefit all populations. Expanding the genetic variability of research has already provided new insights into disease mechanisms and genetic risk. I established the Genetics Awareness Project (GAP), to inform South Florida's Black and Hispanic communities about the value of genetics and its influence on personal health, as well as the value of research participation. From 2012-2014, I organized and led a nationally acclaimed GAP conference titled, "Why We Can't Wait: Conference to Eliminate Health Disparities in Genomic Medicine."

In 2016, my colleagues and I established both Research in African American AD Initiative (REAAADI) focusing on identifying genetic factors within the African American population to detect new targets for drug development and improve the community's accessibility to AD education and the Puerto Rican AD Initiative (PRADI), which aims to include the Caribbean Hispanic Puerto Rican population in AD research. During the same year, my laboratory discovered a frameshift deletion in the *ABCA7* gene was a major risk variant for AD in African Americans (Cukier et al, *Neurology Genetics*, 2016). *ABCA7* nearly doubles the likelihood of developing AD among African Americans, a risk approaching the same as *APOE4* in African Americans. This study definitively showed *ABCA7* as a key modulator of AD in African Americans, further supporting the role of lipid-related genes in AD among African Americans. Recently, my group challenged the research community's lack of appreciation of the importance of diversity by showing that AD risk due to *APOE4* varies based on the ancestral origin of the region of the chromosome where *APOE4* is located. African Americans and Caribbean Hispanics with African heritage of *APOE4* are significantly at less risk to develop AD due to *APOE4* compared to those who inherit *APOE4* from a European background (Rajabli et al, *PLOS Genetics*, 2019). This finding further emphasizes why including diverse groups in medical research is necessary to gain full understanding of how genes contribute to or protect against disease.

As a geneticist my scholarly work has driven me to effect tangible changes in the world. It is my hope that the meaningful discoveries I have made, and continue to make, will be translated into better diagnoses and new treatments for millions of patients across the globe, by facilitating improved future healthcare practices.

Currently I am one of the highest-funded NIH researchers at the University of Miami Miller School of Medicine (UMMSM) and rank nationally among the highest NIH funded genetics researchers. As an elected member of the National Academy of Medicine, I received numerous awards, including the international "Louis D" Scientific Prize from the Institut de France's Academie des Sciences for my Alzheimer's research, the Bengt Winblad Lifetime Achievement Award from Alzheimer's Association and the Snow and Ming Tsuang Lifetime Achievement Award from the International Society of Psychiatric Genetics (ISPG) for my lifelong contribution to psychiatric disease research.

I believe I was at the forefront of understanding why the genetic field's laser-focus on rare, single-gene disorders would not provide the only pathway to positively impacting the treatment of genetic human disease – a fact that became clear much later – my work has had an outsized impact on public health. In 1997, *Newsweek* Magazine named me to "The Century Club," among the "100 people to watch" as we move to the next millennium.

Additionally, I am senior author on the largest-ever Alzheimer's gene study in history (Kunkle et al, *Nature Genetics*, 2019), on which an international team of hundreds of researchers analyzed genetic data from more than 94,000 individuals to reveal five new risk genes for AD and confirm 20 known others. The discovery shared some striking revelations about the cause of the most common form of dementia and attracted national media attention. In March 2019, the NIH Director, Dr. Francis S. Collins, wrote a blog entry about the study, calling its findings "invaluable" for understanding the biological underpinnings of AD and developing new treatments for the disease.

Powerful women, including those in scientific leadership roles, are sometimes called "intense," "bossy," or "power hungry." These are all synonyms for ambition (unflattering as they may be). Let's embrace them and make no apologies for being motivated to succeed!

However, when I'm asked what my greatest accomplishment is, I would always point to my children. My daughter, Danica, after graduating from Duke University, attainted her MD at the University of Miami Miller School of Medicine in 2014. She completed a residency in orthopedic surgery at Columbia University in 2019. She is currently an Orthopedic Sports Medicine Fellow at Duke University. Danica is a superstar. I hope that I have instilled in her the same ambition and belief in her abilities that my father instilled in me.

My daughter recently wrote the following about me: "The best advice my mom has given me can't be put into a simple phrase, but instead is seen in the strong woman she is, and watching her continuously inspire, dominate in her field, succeed and love; there's no better guidance than that."

To me, it does not get any better than that.

The world needs more role models who will actively encourage girls and women from every walk of life to enthusiastically take on leadership roles in science, medicine, and other fields.

As Director of the John P. Hussman Institute for Human Genomics, part of my job is to train early stage researchers while fostering their passion for scientific discovery.

I am doing my best to serve as mentor for the next generation of women in academia.

Will you join me? ■

Kassandra M. Bosire, MD

Assistant Clinical Professor
Residency Program Director
Department of Family Medicine and Community Health
University of Miami Miller School of Medicine

Making the decision to become a physician was an easy one. The journey was not. I completed my undergraduate degree with a major in biology as I competed on a NCAA Division I basketball scholarship while tutoring gross anatomy to make additional income. Saying that I was busy was an understatement. On an athletic scholarship only a 2.0 GPA is required for eligibility. Unfortunately, maintaining that GPA was not going to secure a seat at any medical school, however it was all that was expected of me from my coaches and peers. No one understood my sprints back to the organic chemistry lab or why I was working on my physics II class, rather than my jump shot. My parents emphasized academics and as a student athlete, I was a student first. My competitive spirit always pushed me to do more. Doing more in my mind translated into being not only a premedical science major but also the starting forward for the basketball team. I have never done well sitting on the bench. Completing my undergraduate degree was a high point for my parents (as for most parents, I understand that now as a parent... you are almost off their payroll!!) I was forced to go to my baccalaureate graduation as it was merely a required stepping stone for me. I will be forcing my son as well, if needed. Memorializing milestones with pictures is priceless and showing up for each other is an essential life skill we should all endeavor to master.

I am the child of two amazing parents who worked for the City of Detroit and the State of Michigan all their lives. In their eyes, security trumped dreams any day. Even though my parents knew at a young age I wanted to go into medicine and made significant sacrifices for me and my twin sister, the idea of not working for 30 years for the same employer right out of college, collecting your retirement watch at 55, and living on a pension for the rest of your life, was uncharted territory. As my father said when I graduated, "Take a safe job." For the next five years I worked in the pharmaceutical industry as a bench research scientist.

Never forgetting my dream, "I was supposed to go medical school," I subsequently transitioned from a full to part-time bench research scientist position at Searle Pharmaceuticals. During this six-month period I completed a post-baccalaureate program at The Chicago Medical School, now the Rosalind Franklin Medical School. This allowed me to support myself financially as I was off the parental payroll. My employer, Dr. Komaczar, in recognition of my hard work converted my contract position to a permanent one; with a job description entailing credentials and a skillset that only I possessed. Staying true to my faith, I worked hard and was admitted to Rosalind Franklin Medical School. However, the competitor in me did not stop there. I asked myself questions such as: "Am I not good enough to go through the front door? Am I not worthy?" My inner voice reminded me that I had taken the MCAT twice. My post-baccalaureate program peers said to me "You should just be content with getting in here." That familiar voice of "settling" and getting the "gold watch" only spurred me to send more medical school applications. I settled in at Wayne State University School of Medicine and completed my residency at the University of Michigan in Family Medicine. My mentors were amazing. During residency there were very few women and not one male attending physician that resembled me. Despite that fact, there were many male attendings who openly shared their expectations or better, their lack of expectations, of me.

An indelible example occurred during my PGY-2 year. While I covered the night service, one of my attendings refused to believe I could identify and manage a patient in atrial fibrillation with a rapid ventricular rate by myself. He insisted a fellow must have done it. Staunch in his belief, in front of trembling interns, residents, and staff, he called the fellow to confirm. The fellow calmly indicated he was never consulted, and completely agreed with my plan of care. "This does look like a fellow's work," my attending said. We proceeded down the 8A corridor. Apology never given, interns stunned like in arterial vasospasm and me: humiliated, fatigued, and wounded as we finished rounding on the remaining 8-10 patients. But thank you, Dr. Gupta, cardiology fellow, who supervised me in the CCU for six weeks and saw it as a compliment that he had trained me above competency for a newly minted PGY-2. Throughout my life as an athlete and woman of color I have been accepted by society in this role. We are Olympians, pro tennis players, and professional basketball players. Thank you, Lisa Leslie, WNBA trailblazer, and Althea Gibson, first African American professional tennis player. Being an athlete, a woman of color, and a physician has been a challenge. I've noticed the surprise on non-minority faces and unexpectedly from minority faces when I walk into an exam room or identify myself as the physician. The lens of bias that I am viewed through, or at times invisible, has always been there. It is unconscious bias that comes across in evaluations that separate me from passing and "Sally McIntosh" from honoring. Example: While "Sally McIntosh" may get the best evaluation because she is bright and talented and always has the best answer, she also was always the first one called upon and privileged to get the easy question and/or answer.

While almost invisible, standing tall and athletic at 5'9" I was the one told I had to improve my knowledge base during my evaluation. However, I was the sixth one called to answer the differential on any given diagnosis. The athlete in me has always been accustomed to that; striving to exceed expectations. To harness the spirit of competition and be better than anyone says you are. Accepting someone else's idea of who or what you are limits you. I expect this limitlessness of my residents as their Program Director – to be more than what you or anyone else thinks you are or can be. Do not settle for the "gold watch." Surprise yourself and others. It is such a wonderful feeling of meeting and exceeding expectations that it should be tried frequently in my opinion. My experience as a woman in medicine has taught me that this profession does not have a scenic route and nor should the lives we live outside of medicine. We must always challenge and engage ourselves, our peers and our patients. We perpetually train daily, however in this profession as we journey through it; with our victories and missteps in tow. The scars, more mental than physical, of the stories unmatched by most professions, are forever burned into our amygdalas. We sacrifice our time and our bodies, not because we are so extraordinary, but because we are hopefully and humbly reminded that we have been given an extraordinary opportunity – to literally heal hearts and minds. What a gift! The best gift of all, however, is to train students and residents. Pushing them toward their best as my basketball coaches did for me. Its believing and encouraging my resident when his or her confidence is blown from being called on last or not at all, that you, too, will get through this. I did!!!! I am able to engage in intimate conversations with potentially future hospital CEOs, medical school deans, or maybe even a surgeon general and share with him or her that I have been on your road and I see you and all your potential. That is why I am in academic medicine and where I will stay. It is so worth it. Looking back, academic medicine chose me. I come from a family of teachers and a mother who is a social worker. These are the essential ingredients of a family physician. We are a family of four, with ten college degrees between us. Hard work, teaching, and caring for others is what I was born into. Being a woman and of color in medicine has been faith-challenging and seemingly unsurmountable at times, but the rewards have exceeded my expectations. When a 72-year-old woman from Macon, GA says "Yes" to a much needed mastectomy that she refused from other physicians and she tells you because "You look like my granddaughter, I thought I could trust you," it matters. When I can advocate for the non-traditional resident and see the same spirit I had, not just his board scores, and that same resident goes on to be my chief resident, it matters.

It is of significance because minorities in medicine facilitate improved outcomes for their minority patients. We become health advocates and provide an element of trust that historically has been broken for minorities in this country. My presence on this campus makes me a change agent by drawing and retaining unrepresented minorities to the University of Miami Miller School of Medicine. This small step forward in recruitment and retention assists in restoring confidence to the marginalized minority populations that comprise the majority of the patients we care for at Jackson Memorial Hospital. It also fosters new perspectives on how we solve and meet the challenges of this perpetually stressed health system while improving health outcomes for South Florida and beyond. Diversity brings new ideas, insights, and collaborations not only from talent that may have been born in Jackson Memorial (yes, I have a resident that was born at Jackson!), but from all over the world. This is how we can transform this campus and bring some of the best untapped talent to this institution. So, as a former athlete no longer on the court, I am coaching and enjoying the view from the sidelines. I am honored and humbled to train and mentor some of the best, world-class athletes on the planet: resident physicians. ◼

G. Patricia Cantwell, MD

Chief, Division of Pediatric Critical Care Medicine
Director, Pediatric Palliative Medicine
Medical Manager, US&R South Florida Task Force 2
University of Miami Miller School of Medicine

GOOD GRIEF! I distinctly recall having a serious conversation with my best friend at the wise age of nine and decided I could use these words as the title for a book about all my complicated experiences. I was enthralled by reading about the challenges in the book, *Good Grief, Charlie Brown*. I continue to find wisdom and humor from the Peanuts comic strip characters and honestly can say, "Everything I Need to Know, I Learned from Peanuts." I'd like to share the events in my life to provide a sense of how my career was shaped by the challenges.

In the 1950's my childhood was marked by frustration due to limitations placed on girls who wanted to play sports. I was a "wild child" and dare devil. My parents would often remark how surprised they were when I survived childhood. I grew up in Maine and had a close group of male friends who loved sports and playing military games. Our major challenge was to determine who could swing on a rope from the very highest branch of our massive tree. Thankfully none of us were killed. When I was nine, I was quite devastated to not be included with my closest friends on an organized boys-only baseball team. So instead I accompanied them to daily practice. I brought my glove and played with anyone who played with me. Finally, a coach shouted, "Hey kid, do you want to play?" I was ecstatic to play left field and have our team lauded with the announcement "This is the team with the GIRL!" My aspirations to play football were not as successful. I loved the challenge of contact sports, but as a girl the team wouldn't let me play.

I am so thankful for the discipline and focus I learned from my father who served in the Army during World War II. During my early school years my mother focused on developing my reading skills. I was terrified about speaking up in class and would never volunteer for oral presentations. My mother also taught second grade at my grammar school and conveyed my terror of classroom presentations with my teacher. Afterwards, I quickly was called upon to present to the class although I never raised my hand. Both of my parents were my early cheerleaders and encouraged me to learn invaluable lessons from my failures.

At the end of my sophomore year of high school I had a major "ah ha" moment. During the year's final school assembly, I watched the girl's tennis team receiving accolades for their success and decided I wanted to be on the team, although I didn't play tennis. Over the summer, I spent my afternoons smacking tennis balls against the wall of a local store. I would return to the store late at night, scale the antenna and collect the balls I lofted. I learned the rules of the game on the day of try-outs and miraculously made the team. During my first game, I hit the ball out completely out of the court. I agonizingly recall wanting that game to end quickly. Afterwards, I asked the most talented of our opponents to practice with me and ultimately was rewarded with the #1 position on the team. In 1970 my teammates and I successfully fought for permission to allow the school's womens' sports teams to be presented with the first letter sweaters. I practiced tennis relentlessly, which replaced my focus on academics. I learned mental toughness, concentration, motivation, and teamwork.

As I began to think about life after high school, I decided I wanted to join the Marines. I was absolutely disheartened to meet the recruiter and discover the opportunities for women weren't close to anything that I wanted to pursue. I left the recruiters office thinking "I suppose I could pursue medical school."

I haphazardly approached choosing a college and applied to The College of St. Elizabeth (CSE) after hearing my father say, "I dated a girl who went there, and she went to medical school." I had never toured any colleges and my first day of college was the first time I saw the campus. I almost had a panic-attack realizing there were stringent rules and regulations. I was blessed that during college I learned from some of the most dedicated, passionate nuns who also shared their steadfast faith and devotion. My college years provided me with a very close network of friends from whom I received camaraderie, encouragement, and motivation.

My wild side was not squelched in college. During my freshman year, I snuck into the Chapel and rang the chapel bell. I was chastised by the Dean of Women for this mischievous act, as the bell was only rung after the death of a nun. I was an avid explorer of our college's phenomenal architecture, exploring every nook and cranny of the heights as well as a tunnel system on campus.

I excelled as a biology major yet switched to chemistry in the middle of my junior year. I'm not sure why I made this choice as I realized I had completely disappointed my biology mentors. I also quickly realized my new major came with extreme challenges. I was clueless in my physical chemistry class and had never taken calculus. In retrospect my plan served as a terrific life lesson. Despite experiencing escalating academic stress, I learned exceptional research skills from a Warner Lambert mentor.

My aspiration to get into medical school was put on hold since I wasn't accepted. I found comfort in the Peanuts comic strip depicting Snoopy receiving rejections for his literary attempts. I realized then I had no plans for life after college. At the last minute, my research mentor suggested I apply to the Bowman Gray School of Medicine Pharmacology Graduate School. While meeting the chief of pharmacology, I was able to laugh at myself when he recommended that I stop taking the MCAT so my test scores would not continue to fall to the zero percentile. He asked, "How did you manage to read the English section?" Despite his cryptic comments, he provided me with my next incredible opportunity. He suggested my skills would be better suited in the Department of Anatomy, so I swiftly signed up.

Graduate school posed a tough challenge for me. I had a hard time accepting the denial of my application to medical school. I also realized with my horrific study habits, attaining a graduate education required more than last-minute cramming.

My next career move began when I received a letter from a college friend who was attending medical school at the Universidad Central del Este (UCE) in the Dominican

Republic. She remembered my goals and thought I may want to pursue medical school acceptance outside the US. I jumped at the opportunity, completed two semesters of Spanish, and left after my 2nd year of anatomy. I arrived in the Dominican Republic and had absolutely no idea what anyone was saying. Class attendance was mandatory, during which I wrote letters to friends since I could not understand the professors. Every evening I would painstakingly translate the Spanish notes of a colleague. I studied in English, yet all work and tests had to be completed in Spanish.

I submitted one "Hail Mary" application to medical school at Bowman Gray. I heard nothing and had resigned myself to completing the program at UCE. Fortunately, in October 1977, I received the phone call from Bowman Gray to say someone dropped out of the first-year class unexpectedly. I enthusiastically accepted the open spot and quietly reflected that my unremitting determination had worked.

Once enrolled at Bowman Gray my new classmates were amazed by my experiences in the Dominican Republic: I had my test answers stolen, scraped mud off a store window looking for grades, struggled with my terribly spoken Spanish, and witnessed true poverty. As my expenses were piling up, I was granted the Navy Health Professions Scholarship. I was fortunate to be the only woman in my 3rd year clinical group. My male colleagues and I would let off steam by playing sports including football, handball, and basketball. I was dubbed "Iron Woman" due to my tenacity after spending long hours studying, working, and fiercely competing in sports. I also believe they called me "Iron Woman" due to my reluctance to give up.

At the end of my third year in medical school, I desperately wanted to do something out of the ordinary. I planned an 800-mile bicycle trip from Winston Salem, NC east to the Outer Banks then north to Sea Isle City, NJ. I concocted this plan although I didn't own a bicycle, had never camped, and had not recruited volunteers to join me. When I left Winston Salem, I had never ridden more than 20 miles. I devised a fail-safe plan to track my progress with a med school colleague. I would call every other day, person-to person/collect and would ask for a person with a name derived from my location. I figured out how to change a bike tire. So many people along the way inspired me with their words of encouragement and wisdom while expressing amazement that I was biking so many miles alone.

I completed my pediatric residency training at the Portsmouth Naval Hospital. I was very fortunate to have tremendous mentorship from senior residents and faculty. I treated several highly complex patients and decided to pursue pediatric critical care.

For three and a half years I served as a general pediatrician at the South Carolina Beaufort Naval Hospital. This experience taught me how to speak with frantic parents, how to deal with hospital administration, and I learned how to follow military policies and procedures. Periodically I was expected to provide coverage in the main Emergency Room and to respond to sick calls at Parris Island. With this experience I had come full circle as the Navy also treats Marines. This military experience was also a source of camaraderie, teamwork, and focus.

Since the Navy did not offer pediatric critical care training, I applied for a Jackson Memorial Hospital fellowship, enticed by the awesome windsurfing opportunities. Upon my arrival at Jackson Memorial, there was one attending Intensivist. In 1987, the fellowship required every other night on call and the resident work hours which other fellowships no longer require. I had many mentors from numerous sub-specialties. I learned some of my best procedural techniques and work ethic from our pediatric surgeons. I was worried the experience was not preparing me for the critical care board exam. I decided to explore transferring to a more structured fellowship. I was accepted to Johns Hopkins and believed I had reached the pinnacle of my career. Then Dr. Heinz Gelband, Division Chief of Cardiology asked me, "What do you want to do that for?" He said it seemed I had already found my niche. I turned down the Hopkins fellowship which was a true banner moment for my career.

During my early fellowship years, I used to dread when the social workers talked about patient needs not directly related to invasive technology. I thought our child life specialists were incredibly ignorant when asking my permission to allow a sick child to go to the playroom. I thought that pastoral care providers were only called to give last rites or at end of life situations. I never considered a critically ill child would benefit from psychological treatment. As I struggled with a procedure on a critically ill child, I was stunned when the nurse said, "Don't you think he's had enough?" I remember feeling helpless when an infant died after a heroic resuscitation effort. The family was left behind closed curtains, with only the bedside nurse until transportation arrived to bring the infant to the morgue. There were no supportive team members present only the bedside nurse who wrapped the infant. Time did not stop; other critically ill patients needed assistance. I often struggled with so many options for procedures and technologies and questioned, "When is enough, enough?" I learned it was incredibly heartbreaking for professionals to realize their patients may die.

Initially I wanted to master invasive procedures, but I was enlightened by my interdisciplinary colleagues on the role of comprehensive patient care and the importance of communicating with patients, families, colleagues, and trainees. I did not realize the magnitude these experiences would later have on my career.

In December 1990, I joined the University of Miami faculty. I have always taken to heart how tough training can be which prompted me to focus on making trainees feel more comfortable in the daunting environment of the PICU. I stressed the importance of teamwork and emphasized the value of an interdisciplinary team approach in patient care. My style of practice is the culmination of my life and clinical experience much like the martial arts master. One of my former trainees said I reminded her of the character, Splinter – the wise Rat who mentored the Teenage Mutant Ninja Turtles. My father's influence to always maintain a sense of humor was paramount to my survival in the stressful PICU. My mother's mantra also always guided me: "You should always leave a place looking nicer than when you arrived." I do not think she realized how this would affect me, as I'm now obsessed with picking up trash in public bathrooms.

I learned a tremendous lesson while doing rounds in our open PICU. I realized we were getting wet, and from across the unit I saw a toddler in a crib spraying us with a squirt gun. This encounter made me appreciate our little patients had personalities and needed to play.

My stress from working a hectic schedule in critical care was lessened by having many friends and meeting the love of my life, Dolores, in 1991. I soon had an instant family with two terrific sons, Justin and Brandon. Despite my expertise as a pediatrician, I discovered I knew zip about raising children. The boys were certainly not thrilled with my inability to cook. We decided to have a family-venture and embarked upon Tae Kwon Do training. I valued the lessons from sparring and discipline and mental focus of the martial arts. My personal life included health challenges, which made me tougher mentally and enlightened me with an even greater understanding of the patient experience. I attained my black belt while on chemotherapy, which couldn't thwart my flying side kick. Despite work challenges as a junior attending, I felt that something was still missing. I decided to activate my reserve status as Naval Commander in 1994. I was devastated to have my application declined due to being "physically not qualified." Shortly thereafter, I became medical manager for US&R Task Force 2. This role led to multiple deployments including the Atlanta Olympics, World Trade Center, Mississippi, New Orleans, Mexico Beach, many hurricanes, and the Haiti earthquake. I have been embraced by the Fire Department and continue teaching activities for the FEMA Disaster Medical Specialist Course. For me, there is no greater pleasure than crawling in a rubble pile, working in confined spaces, and pushing the envelope to enhance medical training.

I was determined to present some of our experiences with critically ill pediatric patients at a yearly meeting of CAPC (Center to Advance Palliative Care). I was encouraged to apply for board certification and grandfathered into the field of hospice and palliative medicine. I am so fortunate to work with my nurse coordinator, an exceptional asset. I often joke my critical care skills are key to striving to offer unconventional quality experiences to our critically ill patients

I have been the chief of our critical care division since 1999. I consider myself exceptionally privileged to work with a group of colleagues who need little guidance. I have striven to use my leadership skills to provide a work environment that enables my colleagues to excel in areas allowing their individual attributes to shine. I have continually sought to enhance my own leadership style via a variety of mentors.

Many aspects of our lives shape our persona. My entire family has been incredibly supportive of my career. Laws changed to allow for marriage so Dolores and I could celebrate our wedding with friends, colleagues, and family. My parenting skills escalated in 2001, when we assumed care of our dearest 5 month old grandson, Neiko. My most embarrassing moment as a pediatrician occurred when I confused diaper wipes and Clorox wipes! Neiko survived! Parenting allows me to continue to hone my skills by encountering new trials and tribulations.

My personal journey has been guided by identifying a goal and letting no hurdle deter my progress. Failure and setbacks are to be expected, but I learned my relentless focus will lead to success. The journey must include a working support system. I am humbled by the opportunity I have been given to be involved in the lives of many patients and families. I have witnessed life at its most devastating moments and learned about resilience from colleagues and patients. I have learned to control what we can and to "let go" of aspects out of our control. I have experienced loss of family, friends, and patients. I have learned about tenacity and spirit. Recently I remain inspired by the words of Retired Navy Seal Admiral William McRaven, "Never, ever quit." ■

Gillian Ann Hotz, PhD

Director KiDZ Neuroscience Center
Director Concussion Program
Director WalkSafe, BikeSafe and SkateSafe Programs
Research Professor
Department of Neurosurgery
The Miami Project to Cure Paralysis
University of Miami Miller School of Medicine

On July 22, 1960, I was born into a very close, large, traditional Jewish family in Hamilton Ontario, Canada. I was second of four children, a year younger than my older sister Reesa, and a year older than my brother Martin. Our youngest sister, Lori, was born six years later. As the middle child growing up, I was squeezed between my older sister who our family considered perfect and my younger brother, the only son. From a very early age, I had to negotiate and develop my own identity to compete for the attention the others received.

When a child is born into a Jewish family, he or she is usually named after a family member who has died. Instead, for one of my Hebrew names I was named Golda after Golda Meir, the fourth Prime Minister of Israel (1969-1974) a resilient and brilliant woman. At a young age, I was destined to develop my leadership abilities. My mom was from Cape Town, South Africa, and my father was Canadian, so we traveled a lot internationally and I realized there was a big world to learn about and see.

I believe one incident set the tone for my life's work. When I was four years old, I witnessed my first head injury. It was an accident that happened to my three-year-old brother. On a wintry day as we rode home from school in an old VW minibus, the back hatch opened as the driver pulled away from the curb and my brother fell out onto the pavement. I remember he cried although his brown ski hat protected his head, so he didn't bleed but had a big bump. I comforted him until we got home, and lucky for us, my uncle was a pediatrician. "Dr. Harry Hotz, Doctor for little totz" was inscribed on his office door. Uncle Harry came right over and examined my brother and he was fine. One of the reasons I always wanted to care for children was because of my uncle's dedication and service to several generations of our community's children and their families.

From first grade I remember another formative experience when our class had a spelling bee. Since everyone had to find a buddy, as there was an odd number of children in the class, I did not have one. The teacher lined us up in a row and asked each team to spell a word. If we did not respond correctly, she referred to me as the "odd man" and asked me to spell the word, which I correctly did each time. From that day on, I had the confidence to stand on my own, walk to my own beat, and think differently.

Throughout my elementary and secondary school years, I was always enrolled in enrichment programs, interested in the sciences and surrounded by high achievers, a very competitive group. I still have my fourth-grade science project on the human brain and also saved my fifth-grade project on animal brains. I was always interested in how people think and think differently from each other. If you were interested in the sciences and scored well in high school subjects such as: biology, chemistry, and physics, the next step was pre-med. After my first year of studying pre-med and psychology at University of Toronto and volunteering at Mt. Sinai in the Stroke Unit, I became fascinated with neurological disorders. I observed the multidisciplinary team treating patients and spent time with the speech language pathologist. I remember how she tried to find things the patients could do to bring out their strengths not weaknesses.

My parents were very supportive of my education and encouraged me to apply to US schools for graduate studies. I reviewed speech language pathology graduate programs and was accepted to Boston University, where some of the pioneers and leaders in the field of aphasia, and other neurological disorders practiced. During the 70s and 80s the Boston VA was the place to study with all the leading experts in behavioral neurology. The neurology team was led by Norman Geshwind, MD with Edith Kaplan, PhD, Harold Goodglass, PhD, Martin Albert, MD, Nancy Helm Estabrooks, ScD, and Margaret Naeser, PhD. I was fortunate to be mentored by these leaders in the field, who developed the process approach, disconnection theories, and described frontal lobe disorders.

Following the completion of my MSc degree, Dr. Helm Estabrooks encouraged me to continue my studies and apply to the Boston University School of Medicine PhD program in Behavioral Neuroscience. As part of my research class requirements I was able to contribute to a research study on Traumatic Brain Injury (TBI), and this is when my love for TBI began. Even though each patient was different, there were similarities in some of the physical, cognitive, and psychosocial deficits patients demonstrated.

Along with Dr. Helm Estabrooks we developed two neurocognitive tests; The Brief Test of Head Injury (1991) and the Pediatric Test of Brain Injury (2010). My dissertation work focused on Perseveration in Closed Head Injury. During this time, I learned patient assessment, how to understand their limitations, and determine treatment plans to maximize their recoveries. Daily, I observed this leading group of expert clinical researchers involved in their different projects, writing grants, submitting then waiting to hear if they were funded. It was a process, and still is, but much easier with advances in technology and online applications and submissions. You still must be persistent and keep trying until you succeed. As the years went by, I found children with neurological injury had better outcomes than adults and recovered more quickly. I became very interested in the brain's neuroplasticity and its magic powers, as well as the developing brain.

I completed my doctoral work in the summer of 1992 and was eager to stay in Boston and find a job. Although good jobs were hard to find, I wanted to continue both my clinical and research work with TBI. Since my parents were "snowbirds" from Canada, Miami became my second home. To my good fortune, Jackson Memorial Hospital/University of Miami opened a brand-new Ryder Trauma Center and was looking for brain injury experts. They say timing is everything and I guess I was in the right place at the right time and I met Dr. Barth Green. He was Chairman of Neurosurgery and Medical Director of the Miami Project to Cure Paralysis, at the time. I knew the University of Miami was the place for me. He talked about brain and spinal cord injury research, developing better care for TBI patients, and expanding the clinical research program.

In the early 90's the neurology, and even more so, the neurosurgery department was dominated by men, with very few women faculty. As the years have gone by more women have joined these departments. I never really faced any issues, maybe because of my strong, confident, and just-do-it type of personality. I felt I had a voice and don't think I was treated differently than the male faculty. Although I worked in the department of neurosurgery and was not a surgeon, I knew I had to create something great, and build my own team so Dr. Green would be proud of me. Almost 30 years later, I can say I achieved those goals. Dr. Green has not only been my mentor but also chief advisor, friend, and colleague. He continues to remind me of our privilege to do what we do every day, and we need to lead by example. He is also a great storyteller, humanitarian, and generous with his time and advice.

It was Dr. Green who introduced me to Dr. Kester Nedd, who was looking for a TBI project research coordinator. Kester was a University of Miami/Jackson Memorial Hospital (UM/JMH) neurologist at the time, and the director of neuro rehabilitation. Together, we were the odd couple. He was from Grenada, tall, dark, handsome, soft spoken, and patient. I was short and loud and moved quickly. We made a great team and built a great multidisciplinary team of allied health care professionals, including an occupational therapist, a physical therapist, a speech language pathologist, a neuro-psychologist, a social worker, and a recreational therapist. We took care of thousands of TBI and stroke inpatients and outpatients for about 10 years. Almost 30 years later, we still work together on Tuesdays in our sports concussion clinic. During those years, I learned the importance of working with a team and how each person's contribution is important. From Dr. Nedd I learned that each patient should be treated like a family member and listened to. I have been lucky to have a front row seat and work with one of the best TBI clinicians in the country.

For people to grow and expand their knowledge, they need to evolve, develop, and learn new things. In 2000 the next big change arrived when Dr. Stephen Cohn, Director of Trauma at the time, approached me about creating a program treating children with TBI. I told him we had a great program for adults, caring for them from trauma until they returned to the community, with a specialized intermediate head injury service, which I directed. However, we did not provide these services to children. Dr. Cohn was concerned about an increase in the number of children being seen with traumatic brain injury in our trauma center. Unfortunately, we had the largest number in the country and Dr. Cohn challenged me to find a solution to the problem. My initial step was to put together a task force of community leaders to discuss the problem and determine possible ways to solve it.

In 2003, as the result of the task force's productive collaboration the WalkSafe program was created. And since 2005, it was implemented in all Miami-Dade County (MDC) public elementary schools. WalkSafe (http://iwalksafe.org) was initially funded by the Department of Transportation through Safe Routes to School, a national program focused on increasing the number of children walking to and from school. Over the years, we have received funding from the Florida Department of Transportation, the Children's Trust, and other agencies. The success of the WalkSafe program has positively impacted local communities in the Miami-Dade area, with a 65% decrease in the number of children hit by cars as reflected in the 2017 crash data. The next challenge was to decrease bicycle injuries, and we focused on middle school age children. In 2009, we developed and implemented the BikeSafe (http://ibikesafe.org) program in schools and parks. Currently we are in the process of extending the BikeSafe program to elementary and high schools. Both programs are evidence-based and implemented yearly in MDC and nationally in other high-risk counties. In 2015, we developed a SkateSafe program to educate children about skateboarding in a fun and safe way (http://skatesafe.us) to further our commitment to road safety and primary prevention.

Due to my clinical interest and research work in TBI, as Principal Investigator (PI) I have led many research studies focusing on the improvement of assessment and treatment of children with brain injury. Through these studies and my clinical practice, I have seen and learned a great deal about human suffering and trauma. The best treatment for injury is PREVENTION. In 2004, the distress and pain observed in children and their families led me to develop injury prevention programs and create the KiDZ Neuroscience Center (http://kidzneurosciencecenter.com). The Center focuses on decreasing brain and spinal cord injuries in children and adolescents.

I have always been a big sports fan and grew up watching hockey and Canadian football. In 1996 I went to my first high school football game with Dr. Lee Kaplan, orthopedic resident at the time, now the Director of Sports Medicine at UHealth. I observed how hard these players were hitting each other. During the same year Dr. Nedd and I started the specific clinic for mild TBI and concussion as the number of high school athletes playing contact sports increased, so did my interest in concussion. It was a specific group of injured patients with a main goal of recovery and getting back to play. Since then my attention on concussion in sports has been more focused and committed. Now, I direct one of the best concussion programs in the U.S. Over the years, we developed an expert multidisciplinary team and a 6-step concussion management protocol. In 2012, we developed a countywide concussion program (Uconcussion.com) with the encouragement and support of a high school soccer player, David Goldstein. Goldstein attended private school and wanted the same treatment he received for his concussion to be provided to all Miami-Dade County athletes. We currently manage three counties covering approximately 60 public high schools and 20 private schools, many youth sports leagues, and our UM and other professional athletes.

I share my words of wisdom with the next generation of clinical researchers and suggest to not sweat the small stuff, focus on the bigger picture. My father used to always tell us, try to keep things simple. Try not to complicate your life more than it already is.

It is OK to think differently, which I have done my entire life. I have always encouraged my students and staff to think differently, and to invite new ideas. I also believe a team approach brings diversity and innovation. However, when working with a team, make sure everyone goes in the same direction on the bus. The team should have similar goals and agree on the objectives of the project before beginning. This will reduce drama and chaos and you will achieve great things together.

Also, it is important to continue to engage in learning new things and not only in your field. For many years my cousin, Dr. Myron Weisfeldt, the William Osler Professor, and former Chairman of the Department of Medicine and Physician-in-Chief at John Hopkins University, was invited to be the keynote speaker at the UM medical school graduation. He encouraged the graduating class to attend a lecture or presentation out of their field of study or work once a month. I have done this and encourage my students and staff to do the same. It helps to remember there are other important discoveries and research going on and is good for cocktail party discussions.

Lastly, surround yourself with supportive and positive people, starting with your family, friends, and colleagues. It is also important to have love in your life, which can come in many different forms, traditional and non-traditional. Find what works for you. I have been quite fortunate to have a great family, and most recently, I was encouraged to adopt a puppy. Murphy is now two years old, and even though she is a lot of work and responsibility, she has made me a better and more patient person. Remember the sky is the limit! Carpe Diem! ■

Audina Berrocal, MD

Professor of Clinical Ophthalmology
Medical Director of Pediatric Retinal and ROP
Vitreoretinal Fellowship Director
Bascom Palmer Eye Institute
University of Miami Miller School of Medicine

I grew up in a family of five in Puerto Rico. I had an older brother and sister. My father was the first American-trained retina specialist to practice in Puerto Rico and the Caribbean, and my mother was a laboratory technician. My father was the son of a Spaniard, my grandfather, a very talented man. My grandfather was an engineer, a musician, composer, furniture maker, and a man of all trades. Later in his life, he would design medical instruments for my father. My mother came from a long lineage of strong women. Her grandmother, who I was named after (Audina), was a visionary. In the early 1900s my grandmother lived in a small town, east of San Juan called Loiza Aldea. She was married to a Spaniard who owned cattle, palm tree farms, and a bakery. She worked as a seamstress to make more money. She believed in education and because of her philosophy ALL her seven children were educated. She sent two of her three boys to graduate school in the US. Her oldest son, Ramon Manuel Suarez, studied medicine at the Medical College of Virginia (later in life he became one of the editors of the journal *Blood)* and her second child studied law at the University of Kentucky. Her third son studied commerce in Puerto Rico. The four daughters stayed in Puerto Rico: two became teachers, one a pharmacist, and the other a nutritionist.

It was tio Moncho, as I referred to my grandmother's brother, the doctor, who first inspired me to become a physician. He also supported me as I accomplished my goals until his death in 1981 of renal failure. Before he died, (he was on dialysis and decided to stop), he wrote me a very inspiring letter and left me money for one day to buy my first medical doctor bag. I was 14 years old.

I graduated from catholic school and studied at Princeton University. My brother, who was ten years older than me, attended Princeton. During his graduation, I became enamored with the campus and wanted to follow his footsteps. I was lucky to gain acceptance and was the only student that year enrolled at Princeton University from Puerto Rico. My Princeton years were amazing. I met very interesting, smart, diverse people who changed the way I think and see the world. I graduated with a major in politics and a minor in Latin American studies. At the time, I was interested in politics and policy. The last summer before my graduation I was an intern in Congress. It was then, when I realized studying politics and the reality of politics are very different.

I graduated not really knowing what to pursue next. I thought of becoming a paralegal and began focusing on law school. I had an informational interview with a lawyer for whose family I was a babysitter, and he changed my life. To my surprise, he told me he was not going to give me a job, because he cared too much about me and he thought I should become a physician. After a lot of introspection, I decided to reconsider pursuing medicine.

I completed a few pre-med requirements and worked in a laboratory in Boston doing p53 tumor suppressor gene work in melanomas. During that year, I applied to medical school and decided on Tufts University Medical School where I finished medical school and residency. I spent nine years in Boston until I was accepted for fellowship at the Bascom Palmer Eye Institute, where I have worked ever since.

Tufts University Medical School was the perfect fit for me. My medical school class was diverse, and the medical school was very supportive. Learning medicine in the Boston medical complex was amazing. The quality and sophistication of the medicine practiced there is impressive and my training priceless. I reveled in being surrounded by excellence. In medical school, I began to realize I wanted to become a surgeon. The surgical rotations appealed to me much more than the medical rotations. Surgical subspecialties like urology and ophthalmology were appealing. Tufts had a great pediatric urology department but when I rotated in ophthalmology, my desire to become an ophthalmologist was reignited. When I was a child I worked at my father's office: retrieving charts, filing, dilating patients, helping with minor procedures, and holding steady the heads of patients during laser photocoagulation procedures. Ophthalmology was my first love because my father made his career part of our lives. He took us to rounds during the weekends and would let us watch surgery in the operating room. To this day the smell of Betadine takes me back to his operating room. My father's professional life was part of our lives. His patient's stories were told at the dinner table. His worries and anxieties about surgical outcomes were shared with us. We understood early on, his work was highly valued by others and his expertise needed by many to improve their vision. If he did not make it to a school event, we always knew it was due to an emergency, an unforeseen complication, or a new patient that traveled from far away to see him. My dad loved his job, patients, and employees. It was evident to anyone who knew him, but most importantly to his family.

During the end of my residency and prior to beginning my fellowship my family received the most devastating news. My wonderful, smart, witty, caring brother was diagnosed with metastatic cancer. Only eighteen months later his amazing life came to an end. Finishing my residency, starting my surgical fellowship, seeing my brother's life end and delivering my first daughter comprised the most difficult 18 months of my life. Trying to spend as many weekends with family while I trained was challenging. I come from a family where responsibility and hard work are most important. I worked hard, took a week off for the funeral and used all my vacation and meeting time for my maternity leave. It was not easy.

I believe I came to Miami at the right time. I always loved children and wanted to be a pediatric retina specialist. Unfortunately, at that time, there were very few pediatric retina service centers. In Miami, there was a need for someone to take care of the retinopathy of prematurity service and the pediatric retina service. I was at the right place at the right time and was hired to take care of the prematurity service and slowly I was able to develop a pediatric retina service. I ended up doing exactly what I had hoped for. I worked very hard to develop a service, attending as many conferences as possible. The first five years of my career were difficult since I had three children under the age of five. In those years, I only attended two national conferences and as many local speaking opportunities as I could. The older my children got, the easier it was to attend conferences and present my work. I married a very supportive husband, who happens to be a urologist, and I have a great nanny (15 years). I once read an interview of NPR journalists' Cokie and Steven Roberts that resonated with me. He said "Marrying the right person is the single most important decision you'll every make in your life. Everything else is secondary." I agree.

I cannot speak about my life without sharing the support I received from my sister and my mother. Both very impressive women, they are the source of my strength, perseverance, and grit. My mother is probably the greatest supporter of her children and her family. She is at the core of our strength as a family. Her keen intelligence and her business acumen made our family, and my father, more successful. My sister, a retina specialist, took over my father's practice. She is my ultimate mentor; her constant advice made my life easier. She inspired me with ongoing support to fulfill my roles as a working mom, a retina surgeon, including how to breast feed and offering professional advice on treating retinal surgical complications. I am very lucky to have her as my sister. Unfortunately, that kind of support is not easy to find.

As a young physician, I sought a mentor, and tried to find one mentor who encompassed it all. Throughout my medical career I looked for that ONE mentor and with my youthful naiveté I never found one. I was seeking an inspiring, supportive woman who could help me navigate the struggles one faces in medicine: from deciding what rotations to take, to dealing with a verbally abusive professor, a sexist surgeon, and even an envious colleague. But as a more senior woman in medicine, I realize now that what I was seeking then was impossible to find.

Looking back on my life and career I learned finding mentors is based on situations and rarely is about relying only on one person. People come into your life at moments of difficulty to help guide and mentor you, often during the most difficult times. I call this fluid mentoring (situational). Women, or men, who appear at the right time to give you the advice most needed at that moment. Don't limit your mentors, it might not be the woman you were hoping for, but great mentoring might come from a co-resident, a fellow, your nurse or scrub technician, maybe even from your sister. BE OPEN TO ADVICE! Although I wanted women to mentor me, I realized many of the older women in medicine had such a difficult time and were so jaded by the path they carved for themselves they became uninterested in mentoring others. However, an older woman I consider one of those mentors came into my life at the right time. She told me even mentors who are not good mentors may teach you one very important thing: HOW NOT TO BE!!!

I found this very eye opening. HOW NOT TO BE!!!! There were SO many of these examples in my career. Both men, and women, who educated me by their behavior and showed me EXACTLY how not to behave. I call this negative mentoring. I believe for most young physicians this is the most common mentoring. Nonetheless, I learned even those who "negatively" mentor you may have the most positive effect on your life. You become focused on finding the "best" even among your most complex relationships.

One often does not have the opportunity to consciously choose their mentor. In a perfect world, finding that one person may be ideal. I believe one must always look for the proverbial silver lining. For the younger generations, I believe creating a culture of conscious intention to become the mentor YOU want, is the key to mentoring throughout your life.

For me, some of the most amazing moments of my academic, clinical, surgical and personal path are the opportunities I've had to mentor young women, and men, and to show them how to navigate the difficult waters of a medical career.

As a woman in medicine, I clearly understand the path of women before me was a difficult one. But I know the path I lead will impact those women who come after me. Live consciously!

- Be the mentor you always wanted to have.
- Find the right mentor for the right moment.
- Negative mentoring sucks, but it teaches you valuable lessons and how not to be!
- Giving back should be integral to going forward.
- Remember the struggles of those who came before you.
- Always be grateful.
- Be who you say you are.
- And if marriage is your choice, choose wisely. ■

Kimberly L. Reynolds, MD

Assistant Professor of Clinical Pediatrics
University of Miami Miller School of Medicine
Pediatric Hospitalist
Holtz Children's Hospital at
Jackson Health Center

I cannot recall the moment that I decided that I wanted to be a physician. Most people have some seminal event in their lives that they can point to: the death of a loved one; an ill sibling; going to the hospital with their mom or dad who was a doctor.

I had none of those experiences. But somehow I always KNEW that I wanted to be a physician.

In fact, I wanted to be "a doctor and a teacher" in the childlike way that kids have of wanting to be multiple things at the same time. Who knew that I would end up with that very career as an academic physician.

I grew up in Inglewood, CA in the 80s in a single mother home. Lest you feel compelled to shake your head in pity, know this: my mother, the most courageous person that I have ever known, was not a victim. My father was an alcoholic, and she did not want her children raised in that environment. One day, when I was approximately 2 years old, she made the decision to pour out all of his alcohol and kick him out of the house.

She took life into her own hands and created her own destiny.

My mother was born and raised in Kingston, Jamaica. She worked tirelessly and put herself through nursing school and college in the U.S. She then received a full-tuition scholarship to UCLA, which brought us to California.

After graduating, my mother took on a job as a public health nurse in Compton, CA. My mother had the skills, training, and talent to work ANYWHERE. She chose to work in Compton. She chose to dedicate her time, talents and treasures to serving the underserved in the community at the Headstart center that she ran.

I spent many days at that center with the other children, although I was not enrolled. This experience made a huge impression on me. Even though I was just a child, I recognized that there was nothing different between me and the kids at the Headstart center other than the circumstances that we were born into. There was no difference between me and these children, other than structural factors and historical injustices that hindered their achievement. I knew this with every fiber of my being, even though I didn't have the language to describe it or the knowledge of history to explain it.

I saw my mother transform the center into a colorful and vibrant space for learning. This stayed with me and fueled me. These children deserved to learn and thrive just as much as any other child. Just as much as I did.

I was a good student. In 3rd grade I was tested and my mother was told that I was reading at a high school reading level. In fact, the school wanted to bus me to the local high school for English classes every day. My mother wasn't having it. She knew that I was a talented reader, but didn't want me to have to deal with the social pressures of being a 3rd grader in a high school class. She and the school compromised, and I found myself in the 5th grade English class every day.

This taught me something. Prestige and accolades are not everything. I am quite certain that a Black 3rd grader being bussed to a high school for reading classes would have made the local news. However, my social and emotional well-being were more valuable to her than any B-roll in a nightly news feature.

Books were my entire life growing up. Books allowed me to travel the world when my mother's public health nursing salary didn't. They allowed me to escape the realities of the daily bullying that I received at the hands of a handful of my classmates. I was taller than anyone in my class. I had short, curly hair that could barely fit into pigtails. I didn't have the latest and greatest shoes; despite my mother working hard, our ends often didn't meet. She lived paycheck to paycheck but always taught us to be grateful for what we have.

The incessant bullying affected my self-esteem, as you can imagine. But, it also affected how I succeeded. I no longer worked hard to be at the top of the class, because that had only gotten me bullied and shunned.

I had a new goal-do well, but not too well. Don't stand out. Do what you have to do to survive.

Play small, Kim.

This was not a conscious message that I told myself; rather, this notion of "just enough" was deeply etched into my unconscious mind, only to be unearthed as an adult.

I went to a high school that featured a medical magnet program. I carried the need to not stand out, to blend in, to do well but not too well, with me. I enjoyed high school because it was cool to be smart. I was friends with the popular medical magnet kids, since we had all come from the same middle school. We enjoyed our time there, but I still did just-enough-but-not-too-much all the way to graduation, where I graduated with honors and in the top 10% of my class.

I received a prestigious merit scholarship to attend the University of Miami, the only school that I applied to. College threw me for a loop. I had to work in order to support myself; in fact, I worked 2 jobs in my freshman year! I also needed to juggle work with extracurricular activities and studying.

Just do enough. Don't stand out. Play small, Kim.

But now I NEEDED to stand out. Everyone at UM was pre-med, or at least it felt that way. How could I compete with these students? Furthermore, I did not have mentors or anyone in my family to make connections for me. I was going to be the first physician in my family. I didn't want to give up the dream to serve underserved children like my mother did in Compton.

Riddled with self-doubt, imposter syndrome, and a lack of mentorship, I realized my sophomore year that I was probably not alone. I was sure there were other women of color just like me who weren't sure how they would make it to medical school.

I founded Minority Women in Medicine (MWM) in order to provide shadowing activities, camaraderie, and support for women of color. We started the first ever Coral Gables Relay for Life, implemented and ran Womens' Health Awareness Week, provided mentoring and shadowing opportunities, and held meetings that provided an outlet to our members. To date, it is one of my greatest achievements. We won best new organization and the organization is still having an impact at the U.

I took the MCAT after my junior year of college, but did not apply right away. The reason I didn't apply was multifactorial, but was mostly for 2 reasons: I couldn't afford to apply and I was SCARED out of my mind to apply. Taking a year off from school really allowed me to develop the connections and the courage to apply to medical school. I worked for a year at the Area Health Education Center, a non-profit organization that works to recruit and retain primary care health professionals to serve underserved communities. In this role, I planned and organized health professions education fairs and summer camps for minority students. It was during this year that I fell even more in love with my future profession, and became head over heels in love with primary care. The colorful and vibrant primary care pediatrics clinics affirmed the connection between being a primary care pediatrician and the children in that Head Start center so many years before in my childhood.

Even though I was working, I couldn't afford to apply to many schools. I applied to 5 schools and was accepted to 1 right away and was waitlisted at 2. I vividly remember the Sunday that I received my acceptance letter in the mail. I ran and jumped on my mother – my rock, my encourager, my biggest fan and screamed "Mom!!!! I am going to be a DOCTOR!" She responded "Of course you are." It was a foregone conclusion to her. She never had a doubt in her mind.

Even when I was playing small, she knew I was destined for more.

I remember the first day of medical school vividly. I walked into a very large auditorium with 150 of my classmates. It would be nice to say that they were from all walks of life, but that would be the farthest thing from the truth: they were mostly from one walk of life, and there were a smattering of us who were "others."

Play small, Kim.

My first year of medical school was a major adjustment.

My second year of medical school almost broke me.

My father, the same father who I didn't have a close relationship with but loved desperately nonetheless, became critically ill. I struggled to stay afloat while dealing with a long distance relationship with my fiance (now husband), my father's illness, and the relationship we would never have, all while planning my upcoming wedding.

I was depressed, ashamed, and anxious. It was a lonely time. I didn't tell many people about my struggles. I withdrew from my friend circles and retreated into myself and my studies. I told myself that I was simply busy and being pulled in too many directions. I was again using books as a respite from dealing with the realities of my world at large, albeit now they were textbooks and atlases.

I don't remember who recommended that I see Dr. V, the medical school psychologist. Growing up, mental health was not something that was discussed much, although my mother's masters degree was in psychiatric nursing. It didn't even occur to me initially to seek help. I was carrying those heavy burdens all on my own.

Dr. V. was one of the major blessings in my life. She was the kindest, most compassionate soul to grace the halls of that medical school. She allowed me to cry, vent, and feel the pain – and then helped me to develop tangible resilience strategies.

As I look back on my second year of medical school, I reflect on the incredible pain but also the amazing resilience. I lost 60 pounds that year, planned my wedding, and had the highest grades of my preclinical years.

I took a year off from school and moved to Ohio after marrying my husband, Adrian. It was a year of peace and growth that I am truly grateful for. My father passed away during that year; before he passed away I came to peace with my relationship with him as best as I could.

I absolutely loved my 3rd year of medical school. I was finally able to connect with patients on a deeper level and apply the wealth of knowledge that I gained in my first 2 years. However, this is really where the imposter syndrome began to kick in. Despite this, I was still able to push through and do relatively well. Knowing that I was still a student and that there was an entire team dedicated to the care of the patients helped tremendously.

Play small, Kim.

My 4th year of medical school was a heady time. I had my first child, Israel, during my 4th year of medical school. I matched into my #1 choice of pediatrics residency – Cincinnati Children's Hospital. I walked into residency on the first day fully expecting to be called into the program director's office and told that there was a big mistake. "I'm sorry, Kim. There was a mixup on match day. You are not really supposed to be here."

Imagine the shock on my face when, during my first night on call, the nurse who paged me referred to me as Dr. Reynolds.

Surely, there HAS to be some mistake.

I felt like an absolute FRAUD. I recall going home one day and saying to my husband "One day, these people are going to find me out."

Play small, Kim.

I knew it wasn't productive to consider myself a fraud, but I did not know just how damaging the negative self-talk was contributing to my well-being, or lack thereof. Don't get me wrong… I was HAPPY. I was finally living out my dream. But, I was anxious and didn't fully realize it. It manifested as insomnia. I couldn't fall asleep, or, if I woke up, it was difficult to go back to sleep. I felt like a bad mother when I left my son at home, and I felt like a bad doctor when I arrived at work.

The defining moment was 6 months into my intern year of residency. I was going along day by day, full of anxiety and fear, but hoping that I was masking it all, and playing the role of a doctor well.

Spoiler alert: I wasn't!

My attendings were barely tolerating me (I am somewhat likable, which is the only reason I think I didn't get fired in the first 6 months!). I was stressed out, behind on everything, scared to speak up and answer questions, afraid to ask questions, tired, lonely (sooo thankful for my amazing husband, Adrian!), and basically failing at life. It was definitely a low point for me.

It all came to a head when, post-call after being at the hospital for 30 hours and EXHAUSTED from a busy night on service, one of my attending physicians sat me down and gave me "feedback."

When he uttered the words "I am not calling you stupid, but…" my heart sank. I left that day dejected, defeated, and wondering for the first time in my life if I had made the wrong career move by going into medicine. I remember sitting on the couch of our little apartment in Cincinnati with Adrian and crying my eyes out. I started brainstorming alternative career plans.

It was over for me.

The next thing that I did was what ultimately altered the course of my trajectory in medicine, and by extension, my life. I sat down with one of the senior residents on the team. "I need help," I said, with tears in my eyes. I needed to know how other people viewed me, and needed some actionable tips to help change so that I could improve my performance. To this day I am grateful for this resident (Jayna was her name). She was kind, yet firm: exactly what I needed. She told me what I didn't want to hear yet desperately needed to hear: I came across as incompetent, unsure of myself, and like I didn't know what was going on.

Yikes. It was worse than I thought.

"What do I do?" I asked. How can I change and improve? I wanted to be better for my patients, and I didn't want to develop a negative reputation that stayed with me throughout training. Jayna then gave me the most profound and best professional advice that I have ever received.

She told me that she knew that I felt like I didn't belong and like an imposter. She felt the same way just the year before, when she herself was an intern. If I wanted to conquer my imposter syndrome and change the course of my training, I would have to do what she did: FAKE IT UNTIL YOU MAKE IT.

I looked at her blankly.

"Look," she said. "If you aren't confident with your knowledge, your patients will not have confidence in you; your co-residents will not have confidence in you; your attendings will not have confidence in you. But, most importantly, YOU will not have confidence in YOU. And then, it becomes a vicious cycle."

She explained that the only way to break the imposter syndrome cycle is to fake it. "When you are asked a question, answer with conviction. If you do not know, say what you DO know about the subject, then state what your knowledge deficit is and your plan of action to gain the knowledge. Don't beat yourself up or engage in negative self-talk. Just…do it. Look it up. Gain the knowledge. And continue with your day."

In other words: stop *playing small, Kim*

I was skeptical. But what did I have to lose? What I was doing was definitely not working, so I was willing to try something new.

My next rotation was in the emergency room, which is an imposter's worst nightmare. It is fast-paced and busy, and what you know or don't know will be put to the test. She told me to try out the new method in the ER. I would either sink or swim in the emergency room, and the time to start was now.

I could barely eat the morning before my first ER shift. I was sick to my stomach with dread.

This was it. This rotation would change everything for me, for better or for worse. I kept her words in my mind when I walked in. "Be confident. You are a physician who is here to learn. You can do this." I also kept my favorite scripture in mind: I can do all things through Christ who strengthens me (Philippians 4:13).

I don't remember everything that happened that day, but I do remember this: I thoroughly enjoyed the emergency room! It was fast-paced and somewhat scary, but I actually grew to love the adrenaline rush and the fact that every patient that I saw was different.

But, here's the most important thing. I received amazing feedback from my attendings! I found that they often treated me like a colleague more than simply a learner. I was able to bounce ideas off of them and discuss treatment plans. In the beginning my plans were completely incorrect; if I am being honest, I had no clue what was going on half the time! However, rather than beat myself up or get dejected, I simply filed away all of the learning points and treatment plans so that I could remember them the next time I saw a patient with similar complaints. With time, I became more and more confident.

Jayna was right. I was not a different person than I was a month prior, but my confidence in myself had metastasized and spread, which made others more confident in me. This then led to me learning more, presenting better plans, and getting even more confident. Throughout that rotation and subsequent ER blocks I even became FRIENDS with some of my attendings, and maintain those friendships to this day. The confidence carried over into other rotations, and pretty soon I fell into the swing of things in residency. I will not claim to be the best resident in my class, but I was learning, taking care of my patients, and enjoying myself. I still had some hard days of self-doubt and feelings of insecurity, but Jayna's words continued to echo with me when those days came.

I graduated from my residency program with amazing memories and even more amazing friends. I completely fell in love with hospital medicine during my second year of training, however I couldn't quite let go of my dream of becoming a pediatrician in a brightly-colored clinic and serving the underserved. While looking for jobs, I reached out to my future mentor, Dr. Jeffrey Brosco, who had worked with my mother for years in Miami. He encouraged me to pursue an academic fellowship at the University of Miami. This appealed to me because I now knew that academics was my passion. The fellowship would allow me protected time to develop my research and teaching, and would also allow me to work in clinic AND in the hospital.

During fellowship, my love for pediatric hospital medicine was solidified. I also developed my research interest in cross-cultural care, cultural humility, and implicit bias. I was hired as a Clinical Assistant Professor of Pediatrics at the University of Miami Miller School of Medicine in 2015.

In 2016, I gave birth to my second child, my daughter, Selah. Things were finally coming together in my life!

And then, disaster struck.

My mother, who had been healthy her entire life and retired 3 years prior as Regional Nursing Director at Children's Medical Services, became gravely ill and passed away in 2017. My mother was a devoted mother and grandmother. She loved with everything in her and was the kindest soul I have ever met. I truly mean that.

To this day, I don't know how she did all that she did with such love and grace.

While cleaning out my mother's home after she passed away, I made a devastating discovery. I found a large yellow envelope, the contents of which made my heart shatter. I found my mother's handwriting on multiple pieces of paper.

Leafing through the pages, I realized that this was a book: a manuscript that my mother had written over 2 decades prior. On top of the manuscript was a note to a colleague or a friend (I didn't recognize the name). She asked this person to type up the document for her. Either the person wasn't willing or able to accomplish this task, or more devastating than that, my mother never asked.

She had written an entire book but never even got it typed up, let alone published.

I sat in her living room that day with the contents of my mother's thoughts, hopes, dreams, and aspirations between my fingers and had an epiphany. With all that my mother accomplished, with all of the success that she had, she had more to do, more to share, and more to give this world. However, she did not have the opportunity to share her gift with the world in the way that she wanted, likely due to self-doubt.

I wanted to scream. Why didn't she tell me!!!

Can you imagine the regret of putting something into the world, something as personal and as challenging as writing a book, only to never have it read by anyone? That pain was palpable for me as her daughter; I cannot imagine the pain that she felt.

I wonder if she thought about it often, or simply put it out of her mind?

One thing is for sure. I knew in that moment that my mother would want me to fully walk in my purpose.

Stop playing small, Kim.

My mother lived a great life. She dedicated her entire life to her children and to the children she served, but she had other passions that weren't fully realized.

As a result, I made the decision to fully walk in my purpose and to encourage other women of color to do the same. In addition to my academic work, I am now the host of a podcast called *Productive on Purpose* and have a small online community where I share my struggles with overcoming imposter syndrome and walking in my purpose.

I am grateful for all of the many twists and turns in my journey, as I am now able to help children just like the ones in the colorful clinic in South Central, LA so many years ago. I am able to help physicians and other professionals share their gifts with the world and improve the lives of future generations.

I am blessed to be a blessing to others.

No more playing small. ■

Yiliam Rodriguez-Blanco, MD

Professor, Clinical Anesthesiology
Chief of Cardiothoracic Anesthesia & Associate Vice Chair
for Clinical Research
Department of Anesthesiology/ Division of Cardiac Anesthesia
University of Miami Miller School of Medicine

I was born in the city of Sagua La Grande in Villa Clara, Cuba and attended Serafin Ruiz de Zarate, the Higher Institute of Medical Sciences, and completed my training in 1996. A year before my graduation, my grandfather, a former political prisoner under Castro, was granted asylum in the U.S. and moved here with 17 members of my family, including my parents and younger sister. Due to Cuba's restrictions on doctors emigrating, I was unable to join my family, and had to remain behind with my husband, Jorge. However, my desire to join my family never wavered. Three years later, my father died from a myocardial infarction at the age of 48. As a result of the political differences and travel regulations between countries, I was not able to say goodbye. My grief over the loss of my father, and the feelings of guilt for not being able to help him, (after all I was a doctor) were almost unbearable.

Over two years, I attempted to leave the country 15 times, and in spite of suffering through four Cuban Coast Guard detentions and multiple threats, finally in 2001, I made it out of Cuba with my husband and my then two-year-old daughter, Jeimy. The crossing was terrifying. In the middle of the Atlantic on rough seas, the boat began to malfunction. Running short on gas and with minimal provisions, (one gallon of water, two bottles of soda, and some crackers for a group of 26 people) the crew decided they needed to drop us off on a small unidentified island, many miles from our intended destination. As adults, my husband and I chose to take this risk, but my daughter? As a mother, she was my greatest concern. I pled with the crew to take her with them, fearing I would die on that desert island along with my loved ones. Due to good luck and honesty, two days later the crew returned for us. With nothing but luck and sheer determination, one of my dominant personality traits, poetically, we arrived in the US on July 4th, Independence Day!!

The U.S. and my family welcomed us with open arms. However, only after a few days in the U.S., I realized my predicament. I was a small-town island girl who didn't speak English with a profession I couldn't practice, with little or no money and responsible for raising my daughter Jeimy. It was amazing how many people were quick to tell me to forget my dreams of practicing medicine in the U.S. Repeatedly I was told I would never be a doctor again. It was emphasized I "was" a doctor back in Cuba but not here, it was time to face reality and move on. I still have vivid memories of my grandfather telling me to ignore these people. My family had complete faith in me, and my father was watching out for me from heaven. Again, I drew on my strong determination and didn't consider failure an option. With the support of my family, and a good friend who loaned his study materials, an old computer and using an old Webster's dictionary, I began studying for my USMLE tests. Six months later, I passed both STEP 1 and 2 and was applying for the clinical skills exam (CSA). I still had one small problem. By this time, I was able to read and write English, but I was unable to speak more than a few words. Frankly, I could barely understand someone speaking English without a Cuban accent! I began to prepare for my next challenge. I created a guide with multiple case scenarios and common medical questions, and with a friend also preparing to take the test, I started practicing patient interviews on friends and family members, and anyone who spoke English.

After successfully passing the last test and becoming ECFMG-certified, I began the challenge of finding a medical residency. I knew to be competitive, I needed more than good test scores. After all, I was a woman in my early thirties starting my career from zero, in a foreign country where no one knew me. I knew my English was terrible and I had to do something to be more competitive.

In 2003, I applied to volunteer at the University of Miami Division of Clinical Research in the Department of Anesthesiology. After performing well as a volunteer, I became a paid post-doctoral research fellow. I still remember my first job interview with Dr. Keith Candiotti, who at the time was program director and vice chair for clinical research. It was almost a one-way conversation. He asked me many questions, and my answers began with either a long pause or with my favorite word "ok," even when ok was not an answer to the question. I told him I was having trouble understanding his accent. He insisted he didn't have an accent; as he was from Missouri.

Much later I asked him why he took a chance on hiring me, an unknown female foreign medical graduate who couldn't speak English. He told me anyone who scored 99 on the USMLEs and didn't speak the language had to be given a chance. I was banned from speaking Spanish in the office or the hallways, with the intention of improving my English to overcome my fear of speaking publicly. At first, I was assigned a job performing computer data entry but was quickly moved to working with patients in clinical trials. Aside from my struggle with English, I had to learn essential things like how to use a copy machine, fax a document, send emails, and drive a car. Trying to locate a bus route in Miami-Dade County was not easy. On the positive side, I learned about the world of basic science and clinical research. Most importantly, I learned the difference between "good" and "really good" chocolate.

While conducting clinical research in the operating room, I fell in love with anesthesiology and in 2005, began my residency training after matching at UM. Ironically my medical training would take place in the same hospital where my father passed away so many years ago. I believed this meant he was still watching over me.

My interest in pursuing academic research continued to grow and during my residency training I participated in many resident research competitions, grand round presentations, writing abstracts and submitting manuscripts. In 2009, I completed my training and was awarded the "Highest Academic Performance Award" in my residency class. In 2010, I became board-certified and nationally ranked fourth on the written board exam among more than 6,000 applicants. In 2011, after my residency, I completed a fellowship in Cardiovascular and Thoracic Anesthesiology (CVT) and attained national board certification in advanced Perioperative Transesophageal Echocardiography

(TEE). I was amused by how my life had come full circle. In 2013, I became the division chief for the same cardiovascular and thoracic anesthesiology service that trained me, in the same hospital that cared for my father.

My research career in anesthesiology really started in 2004, and since then I became even more interested. I am a co-investigator, or the primary investigator in over 93 clinical trials, including funded-studies and investigator-initiated trials. My research results include authoring over 50 peer-reviewed publications, and on many as first or senior author. I have co-authored book chapters, and I am working on several new projects, always trying to prove myself to my colleagues. I derive great pleasure and satisfaction from teaching medical students, residents, and fellows rotating through our CVT anesthesia rotation, emphasizing cardiac physiology and echocardiography. I'm honored to assist medical students as they learn the material, I found so challenging, due to my language barrier.

In 2010, in recognition of my research and teaching, I was appointed the Department of Anesthesiology's Director of Clinical Research. Eight years later, I was promoted to the Associate Vice Chair for Clinical Research. Each year, I mentor and direct four upper-level anesthesiology residents in clinical research and assist junior faculty. Currently, mentoring students in my professional life is new. After spending many years advancing my career; now I help build my students' careers. Each year to assist our residents in recognizing the benefits of presenting their research, I guide them on developing presentations for the Gulf Atlantic Anesthesiology Resident Research Conference (GAARRC). Annually, the GAARC is held in a different Southeast U.S. city. Nothing else gives me greater satisfaction than one of my students successfully presenting and winning a competition. Honestly, I am even more proud when it is one of my students who speaks English as a second language. Seeing women from other countries undertake this challenge, evokes memories of my hard work and struggle to accomplish my goals.

In 2014, due to my academic productivity and the support of the faculty, I was promoted to associate professor of clinical anesthesiology and then advanced to professor, four years later. My colleagues often remind me regardless of gender, that my eight-year history of academic advancement set records in the Department of Anesthesiology. Currently, as the only female among over 100 faculty with the rank of professor in our department; I continue to work to improve the female to male ratio, with the support of my department and chair.

As a physician, my true love is clinical medicine. In addition to my academic pursuits, three to four days a week I deliver clinical care in the operating room and respond to my full share of calls. While I participate in many cases, I prefer to care for cardiac patients. I feel most at home in the operating room and often intentionally seek out complex and challenging cases. I find little in life more rewarding than successfully guiding the care of a critically ill patient so they can eventually leave the hospital in better health. As the chief of this practice, I run the OR schedule allocating staff resources between two hospitals and several cardiac surgical services and keep the resident and fellow training on everyone's radar. While often reminded I am the sole woman leading a group of all-male CVT anesthesiologists and operating with a team of all-male CVT surgeons, I rarely let that enter my thoughts. In the end, everything takes second place to patient care. Making sure patients receive the highest level of care is the hallmark of our department.

During my free time, I enjoy spending time with my family. It is clear life is short and there is no better time than today to spend hours with your loved ones. I also adore reading almost anything and visiting museums. I found my favorite painting in the Museum of Fine Arts, in Boston; "Mother and Child in a Boat" by Edmund Charles Tarbell. It reminds me of my journey across the sea many years ago with my daughter, holding her tightly in my arms, telling her everything would be okay. Another reward I didn't expect (after my struggle to achieve) is that my daughter has decided to follow in my footsteps by becoming a physician. Currently, she is a pre-med student at UM. I have no doubts she will surpass my achievements and accomplishments.

In conclusion, my life at UM is rewarding on so many levels. I am currently working on several academic projects and aggressively pursuing additional research funding and new clinical challenges. The practice of surgery and anesthesiology continually change and staying ahead of new procedures and trends occupies much of my time. I can only hope my effort has and continues to justify the confidence my family, my department, and colleagues have shown me over the years. Perhaps my story, as a small town Cuban female doctor who couldn't even speak English but achieved all and became a professor at a world-class American university, will inspire women nationally and internationally, to go for their dreams and never let anyone tell them to give up. You can do it. ▧

Joan E. St. Onge, MD, MPH, FACP

Associate Professor of Clinical Medicine
Senior Associate Dean for Faculty Affairs
Interim Chair, Department of Medical Education
University of Miami Miller School of Medicine

My path to this point in my career has been quite different than other physicians. In my early teenage years, I dreamed of becoming the first woman US president or having a substantial role on the international stage. My earliest desires included having a career and a very busy family and all that comes with it. Somewhat unrealistic? Yes, but I had no doubt that I could have it all, growing up in a large family with great parents to guide me. I never thought there were barriers to accomplishing my goals. And interestingly, in those early years, I never thought becoming a physician was part of the plan. Here is my story.

My parents met when my father was studying at Catholic University. They married on the day after his graduation. They had eight children, and I was the seventh. My parents were my first and most important role models. My mother was a master of organization, a great friend, and a passionate person with very high standards. My father was fair and calm and never said a disparaging word about anyone. My education began during our nightly dinners. Everyone had something to say, and no one waited for their turn to speak. Opposing viewpoints were allowed, and sometimes heard, depending on who could speak the loudest. As I grew up and entered the workforce, I had to train myself to allow people to finish speaking - it just doesn't come naturally. Anyone who has grown up with many siblings knows that brothers and sisters can be frank when sharing their opinions and we quickly learn to filter out stupid or thoughtless comments. I began my resilience training at an early age.

My father's job sent him all over the world. We moved to Europe twice before I went to college. I lived in The Hague for two years and started my education there. Our next move occurred while I was in high school. Moving from a small town in New Jersey to Brussels, Belgium as a teenager was a transformative experience. Leaving the confines of my town happened at just the right moment. I was ready to be independent (I was fifteen!) and exploring the world sounded just about right to me. During that year, I met some of my closest friends, became more self-confident, grew very close to my younger brother, realized that my parents were very cool and was extremely happy. However, the year ended in tragedy for my family. In late spring one of my older brothers, a first-year college student, was diagnosed with hepatocellular cancer and died very soon after his diagnosis. My journey to becoming a physician began here.

I was a very successful writer in high school, and initially chose to pursue English literature as a major. I matriculated to my father's alma mater, Catholic University, and began my sojourn in Washington DC. There is a saying among guidance counselors that there is a college for everyone – and Catholic was the one for me. Catholic University in the 1970's was a place of activism. As a student, you were expected to engage in community service, speak for those with less, and engage with the administration and faculty. Located in our nation's capital, I went to school with future politicians, governors, representatives, and mayors. We lived and breathed politics, worked on campaigns, worked for congressmen and senators, and had a lot to say. I was exposed to the broad liberal arts curriculum of the school. Plato, Shakespeare, Aristotle, Dietrich Bonhoeffer were subjects of study in our first year. This was followed by a never-ending list of requirements in philosophy, history, arts, literature, math and science. It was challenging and we thought some of it was irrelevant, but in the future those courses would prove invaluable.

After abandoning the idea of being an English major (no jobs for English majors!), I studied politics, and then economics. It was through this course of study and the extracurricular activities that I started to meet role models on my leadership journey. As a freshman and sophomore, I worked for my representative in the U.S. Congress. Millicent Fenwick was a maverick on many fronts. https://www.nytimes.com/1992/09/17/nyregion/millicent-fenwick-82-dies-gave-character-to-congress.html. We knew her as a pipe-smoking, outspoken woman who would, despite her wealth, calculate her gas mileage each time she filled up her car. In her sixties, she became a member of Congress. She was a Republican AND was an outspoken progressive and champion for women's issues. I worked as an intern in her office, doing everything from answering constituents' letters, writing reports, and attending meetings with her, which included traveling in the back of DC police cars to get us from one place to another.

In my junior year, I moved to London and worked in Parliament for Patrick Cormack, a Conservative who represented the Southwest Staffordshire district. Compared to Mrs. Fenwick, who had a large staff, he had no staff. His wife Mary was his transcriptionist, and I was his sole staff member. My duties ranged from walking through the underground passage from Old Scotland Yard to the House of Commons each day to collect mail, writing reports on the SALT II ICBM missile reduction treaty, investigating constituent issues, and sitting in the balcony of the House listening to Prime Minister's question hour. I met Margaret Thatcher at a reception we organized for the conservative members of Parliament, held in the Jerusalem Chamber in Westminster Abbey. In my last few weeks in London, I celebrated my 21st birthday with Mr. Cormack and his family on the Strangers' Terrace overlooking the Thames. Upon my return, I wrote a piece for my college paper on the difference between Congress and the House of Congress outlining my experiences in these two worlds and began working on the next stage of my career.

So how did I end up pursuing medicine? Since my teenage years and the death of my brother, I continued to think about a career in medicine. Quite frankly, I was afraid that I wouldn't be successful. Reading, writing, engaging in discourse was easy for me, and I worried that my talents were only in the liberal arts, not in science. While I had done well in my calculus and required science courses, I feared failure. Putting a voice to my desire to become a physician would be entering a world of uncertainty. I thought for many hours about it, silently thinking of the obstacles that may lay ahead. Slowly I faced the reality that I would certainly regret not pursuing the path I had quietly considered for many, many years. I remember the conversation I had with my father one week after I graduated from college. "I would like to become a doctor," I said, "and I need to go back to school." My parents were totally supportive, and soon I was back in school fulfilling the rest of my science requirements. Within two years I was matriculating to Georgetown University (GU), where I remained for the next 21 years. GU was a great place to learn and to train in internal medicine. The entire medical school experience was challenging but incredibly rewarding and memorable. We selected our teams in third year, and this group went through every rotation together. I will never forget those experiences. Following graduation, I stayed on at Georgetown. My internship was a time of exponential growth coupled by unending exhaustion. Thirty-six hours in the hospital was followed by one night off, and a full day ahead. Duty hours were just that – more and more hours. And while the exhaustion was an ever-present companion, and eroded our well-being, it was partially balanced by a sense of teamwork that existed in our environment. As residents, we controlled the hospital at night. We followed patients from admission to discharge. While we learned to survive the hours and the disappointments, I know I suffered from what is now called burnout. My ability to look at a patient at 5 AM was different in the first weeks of internship than it was a year later. And while I was the Intern of the Year for my class, I can still recall the sheer despair I felt in February of that year, wondering if the experience was worth it. I consider myself very lucky to be one of those that bounced out of the burn-out phase and into a very fulfilling residency experience.

Personal Growth and Professional Challenges

I ended my residency training as the chief resident in medicine at GU and decided to pursue a career in academic internal medicine. I continued at Georgetown as a faculty member. Just before I started as an attending, my husband and I married. It was a great time in my career and in my personal life. We had our first child, John, during my third year on the faculty. Our second child, James, was born three years after. At work, I enjoyed attending to my patients, in both the inpatient and outpatient worlds. I worked with medical students and residents. My practice and my reputation grew. In addition to my practice, I began to play a bigger role in education. I worked with many talented educators and viewed my close colleagues at Georgetown as role models. Ray Mitchell, the current Dean at Georgetown taught me how to think big and garner support for my ideas. My colleague throughout my training and as faculty, Dr. Princy Kumar, now professor of medicine and associate dean for students, taught me to have high expectations for your learners and helping them achieve was the mark of a good educator.

I was provided with many opportunities to lead while at Georgetown, and by the early 2000's was the division chief of general internal medicine, the internal medicine program director, and the clinical services vice chair. While I believed I could simultaneously do many things, looking back on this time in my life makes me anxious. I was totally overextended, and my work-life balance was totally out of whack. I had two young children, my husband was in a very busy hematology oncology practice, and I was spending more and more time at the office. The early 2000s were also very unsettling times. September 11 happened, followed by the anthrax terrorist attack, followed by the Virginia sniper in my community, which left us afraid to go out of our homes for months. Facing the reality of how ephemeral life is, many of us were taking stock of our lives. Reflecting on where I was in my life, I felt a deep sense of unease and loss of purpose. I realized I had to take more time for the individuals who counted the most, and the success of my children was our ultimate responsibility. I realized I was easily replaced as a physician to my patients, as an educator of residents and students, but not as a mother or a spouse I decided to make a radical change – I announced my retirement from Georgetown to pursue a less hectic life as a mother – whose work was at home, and focus on the success of my family. My retirement lasted for about 14 months, at which time my children, then aged 11 and 8, told me I needed to go back to work.

In 2005, I went back to work totally renewed. I decided to pursue a job at George Washington University (GWU) in the Division of General Internal Medicine. The chair of medicine at GWU, Alan Wasserman, supported my request to work until 2 PM each day, and I was awarded permission to design my day. I worked seeing patients each day until 12 and taught in the afternoon. I worked in a new system and met new colleagues. I saw my family more. I eventually transitioned to full time work, and continued to enjoy patient care, teaching, and gradually engaged in more medical education and administration. I was able to pay it forward for my colleagues and take over as the interim program director at GWU, to allow the program director, a good friend and role model, Dr. Gigi El Bayoumi, to pursue a well-deserved sabbatical. The atmosphere, the people I worked with, and the patients I cared for were a perfect blend for me. I loved working there. Around that time, my husband made the decision to retire, and we made a strategic decision to move to Florida before our boys started high school.

We moved to Florida in 2008. It was not an easy move. I missed DC, and so did the boys. In 2009, I decided to move from my initial employer to the University of Miami. Moving here taught me a lot about navigating a new system, making smart choices, and working toward a common goal. I began working on the regional campus, with an amazing group of educators, including Dr. Danny Lichtstein and Dr. Gauri Agarwal, who continue to lead the regional campus. While there, our team worked together on the development of the regional campus, the transformation of the UM at Florida Atlantic University curriculum into the four-year MD/MPH program. I led the expansion of the graduate medical education programs and worked with Holy Cross Hospital to develop new graduate medical education programs. I moved from the regional campus to the Miami campus in 2013 and began to lead our graduate medical education efforts at Jackson Memorial. Since then, my work at Jackson has allowed me to build on the lessons I have learned: burnout is real, but does not need to define one's career, and, despite the love of what we do for our patients, work-life balance is paramount to success. As faculty and as an institution, we can acknowledge this without diminishing our overall commitment to excellence.

Reflections

I decided to become a physician based upon my first very tragic interaction with the medical profession. My family's history intersects with some of the greatest advances in medicine over the last 50 years. My parents had Rh incompatibility. In 1949 there was no treatment, and they were told to have only one child. After their third child, exchange transfusions were performed immediately after birth. My brother contracted Hepatitis B or C as a neonate and died of the consequences 19 years later. I have been privileged to see advances in research uniquely tied to my family history. RhoGam, the Hepatitis B vaccine, treatment of hepatitis C, and advances in liver transplantation make it highly unlikely that what happened in my family occurs today.

I consider myself part of the first generation of women physicians who really tried to do it all. Those of us who came of age in medicine in the 1980s and 1990s were offered very few opportunities to discuss critical issues with more experienced women. My medical school class was 24% women, and women comprised more than 50% of my residency class. We would have benefited from more women role models and mentors, especially during critical times in our professional careers. Today we know that mentors and role models are not enough in achieving great success. We need sponsors and coaches to round out our team. My recent decision to move from graduate medical education to faculty affairs is grounded in the idea that our faculty, who are vital to the success of the institution, have been left out of the work-life balance conversation. Our faculty need mentoring, coaching, support for their work-life issues, and a visible path to their future goals.

Who were my role models and mentors? My parents, my husband, and my children. What they taught me cannot be summarized on a page. Millicent Fenwick taught me that age does not limit you from advocating for your beliefs. My Georgetown colleagues Princy Kumar and Ray Mitchell were great role models. Alan Wasserman let me come back to medicine on my own terms and allowed me the work-life balance I needed. I hope I can do the same for others. Danny Lichtstein and Lanny Gardner stand out for their guidance and advice as internists and educators.

This is my advice to my junior colleagues. Believe in yourself. Know your priorities and expect them to change as you move through your life. Look for mentors both in medicine and outside of our profession. Every so often take time to reassess. Listen to your family – they know you best. And don't be afraid of change. It happens. Embrace it. ∎

Sheila Ann Conway, MD, FAOA

Professor & Chief, Division of Orthopedic Oncology
Program Director
Orthopedic Surgery Residency & Musculoskeletal
Oncology Fellowship Programs
Department of Orthopedic Surgery
University of Miami Miller School of Medicine

As a professor of orthopaedic surgery at the University of Miami Miller School of Medicine I specialize in musculoskeletal oncology. My clinical practice is focused on oncologic surgery in children and adults including benign and malignant bone and soft tissue tumors (sarcomas), locally advanced skin cancers, and metastatic disease to bone. As chief of the division of orthopaedic oncology, I mentor two orthopaedic colleagues, promoting the growth of their clinical practice, research, and academic endeavors. In addition to a busy practice, I am the program director for the orthopaedic surgery residency and musculoskeletal oncology fellowship programs.

My research interests include clinical studies relevant to my oncologic practice and focus on prevention of medical errors and the safe practice of orthopaedic oncology. As nearly half of patients with soft tissue sarcoma present to cancer centers following an inappropriate surgical procedure ("unplanned excision"), both research and education are essential to optimizing care in patients with these rare neoplasms. I have also looked critically at the educational changes and innovations implemented in our residency program and have published this growing body of work. In 2016, I was honored with the Department of Orthopaedic Surgery's "Outstanding Teacher Award," awarded by the resident group in appreciation of my dedication to resident education.

In 2008, immediately after my academic appointment, I became involved with the residency program. I was inspired by my own personal struggle to integrate into the least diverse specialty in all of medicine. Education and mentorship are critical components of my academic mission and provide me with immense job satisfaction. As my passion for medical education has grown, so has my appreciation of the healthy work balance this provides to my oncologic practice. Many of my leadership positions and research endeavors are focused on medical education and improving the inclusiveness of my surgical specialty, my department, and the institution.

The unique surgical challenges specific to orthopaedic oncology initially attracted me to this unusual subspecialty and keep me engaged in my daily surgical practice. Operating all over the body on a variety of tumors and in all age groups, the clinical problems are complex and require creative and innovative surgical solutions. For example, resection of a large bone sarcoma often leaves a structural skeletal defect which can be reconstructed using complex modular metal implants, allograft, autograft, or customized implants. Every surgical case is different and each reconstruction has its own challenges requiring creativity, complex planning and innovation to determine an oncologic and functional *individualized* patient solution.

This multidisciplinary field also mandates a team of specialized physicians (radiation oncologist, medical oncologist, pathologist, musculoskeletal and interventional radiologist) to deliver comprehensive and coordinated care. The most complex oncologic cases demand multispecialty surgical teams, which may include cardiothoracic, plastic, vascular, and general surgeons. This team-based approach has facilitated my collaboration with a varied population of medical professionals, allowing me to open my workplace to more diversity despite the severe lack of diversity in my primary specialty.

Without medical professionals in my immediate family, I didn't receive any guidance on how to navigate the medical field, nor have I had the privilege of working directly with a senior female orthopaedic surgeon. Thankfully, my upbringing and experience as a competitive athlete provided me with the grit and skills needed to persevere. Due to my father's occupation, I moved extensively throughout my childhood, relocating all over the country and even twice within one year. I adapted by throwing myself into the pool (literally) and chose swimming as my competitive sport. Through every relocation my focus on athletics grounded me and served as an essential physical outlet for me, simultaneously teaching me self-reliance, the value of time management, and the importance of perseverance.

My hard work paid off. I qualified for the Olympic Trials in 1988, 1992, and 1996 and earned the opportunity to represent the U.S. in the World University Games in Sheffield England. I received a full athletic scholarship to the University of California at Berkeley (UCB) where I achieved All-American honors and was elected team captain. In 1996, I received the Anna Esplanchade Award, presented to one UCB female student athlete in honor of their excellent attitude in an athletic endeavor. I was fortunate to have a long and successful athletic career and value the skills and my memories of the experience. Interestingly, it was orthopaedic surgery that provided me with my ticket to the Olympics. In 2016 I served as an on-field physician at the Rio Summer Olympic Games!

While I intended to continue competing after my collegiate eligibility ended, my predetermined trajectory to train for the 1996 Olympic Trials was slowly but definitively re-directed towards a future in medicine. I became as committed to this quest as I had been in competing for a spot on the Olympic swimming team. I attended Temple University School of Medicine and initially was interested in women's health. A single week rotation on orthopaedic surgery was enough to change my path, as the physical, manual, and puzzle-solving nature of orthopaedic surgery appealed to me in a way no other surgery had. My entry into the orthopaedic world was challenging and I struggled to catch up to the male applicants as they perceived my decision to pursue this specialty as a "late" arrival. Many of my colleagues had fathers in the profession and had planned to pursue orthopaedic surgery from a young age. Several male surgeons and students discouraged me because of my gender as well as their perception of my late interest in the specialty. Fortunately, pediatric orthopaedic hand surgeon, Dr. Scott Kozin, was pleased to see a woman with a genuine interest in the field and provided the essential guidance I needed to successfully match into this competitive specialty.

I completed my residency in a small orthopaedic surgery residency program, the oldest orthopaedic training program in the state, that never had a female faculty member or orthopaedic resident. Coincidentally, a close relative was a patient of an orthopaedic surgeon at the program, and when told I matched with his program, he replied, "That's not possible – we don't have women in orthopaedics at our program." My relative responded with great pride, "Well, you do now!"

My first days as an orthopaedic surgery resident were incredibly bizarre, and I was unprepared for the singular focus on me due to my gender. Everyone was aware of a new female orthopaedic surgeon starting and all had an opinion about it. As I assumed my new position it became immediately clear the spotlight would be on me for the next five years. I compliment my co-resident who also tolerated this unwanted attention. Fortunately, he brought a light-hearted attitude to the situation and joked that our genders became our most defining feature.

As the first female orthopaedic surgeon, I put an immense amount of pressure on myself to perform. In a profession where there is little room for error, I allowed myself none. I knew I was being watched and I was committed to doing my absolute best. These efforts were noticed and appreciated by the majority of faculty and I was quickly considered one of the strongest residents in the program. Several excellent and supportive male mentors provided me with personalized surgical training, professional advice, and guidance, so I could thrive. And while my overall experience was positive, it was very different than my male colleagues.

Some of the differences were small and cumulative, while others were more substantial and discouraging. For example, as I entered a room full of male orthopaedic surgeons there would be silence, which over time became deafening. It became apparent when I entered the room, I had either interrupted an inappropriate joke or "locker room talk." I was having an impact on their culture. My mere presence changed the tone of the conversation in a way many resented. The more entitled faculty made it clear to me they disliked screening their jokes and did not appreciate the behavioral restrictions that *my presence* seemed to demand.

During my residency, we began a rotation at a new hospital with a new group of orthopaedic faculty and I was the first resident at this new hospital. After introducing myself in the operating room on day one, with indignation the orthopaedic surgeon announced, "We've been trying to get an orthopaedic resident for years. We finally succeed and they send us a girl." I was speechless and the room fell awkwardly silent, except for the sound of him laughing at his own joke. Unfortunately, this misogyny *did* impact the surgeons' engagement with my education and my surgical exposure on this rotation suffered. Afterwards, the male residents who followed me reported amazing surgical experiences and this became a favored educational rotation.

Without female mentors, I taught myself how to navigate these scenarios and sometimes I got it right. I was critical of myself in how I handled these daily road-bumps, constantly questioning my own responses – holding myself to an unrealistic standard. As my residency concluded I was asked to participate in the resident selection process and realized this opportunity would influence the program's future hires. I quickly learned that my impact on the culture was complex. All female candidates who followed were measured by my performance which became the new standard, while male candidates were discussed and compared with the entire applicant pool. Subsequently many highly competitive female candidates were overlooked, usually due to the all-male selection committee's perceptions regarding the candidacy of any female orthopaedic surgeon. It was at this moment I knew I would pursue resident education and program leadership in my career.

My commitment to improving diversity and inclusiveness in orthopaedic surgery remains central to my academic mission and I am proud of the impact I've had on my work environment. In 2008, I was the only female faculty in the Department of Orthopaedic Surgery, with a residency program of two women out of 35, and a struggling reputation specifically among female applicants. In 2019, our department has six female faculty (one professor, one associate, four assistant professors) and four female residents in our training program. And, the culture is changing nationally and locally with multi-pronged efforts such as a seminar I directed on "Women in Orthopaedics," sponsored through the SEEDs "You Choose" Leadership Award. On a state level, I have successfully advocated for and participated in the establishment of a novel diversity committee within the Florida Orthopaedic Society, with both male and female leadership support.

I have also witnessed change in my field through the bravery and strength of women who have come before me and continue to break glass ceilings. I recently returned from the 2019 Annual Meeting of the American Academy of Orthopaedic Surgeons, at which Dr. Kristy Weber became the first female president of this 83-year-old leadership association. Currently with only six percent female representation in this specialty, all the women strategically sat together and showed immense support for Dr. Weber. If there was anyone in the crowd not moved by her exceptional presidential address on leadership and inclusion, afterwards it was drowned out by the long and loud standing ovation from the women and minorities in the audience. These are the moments, as women, we must embrace and hold onto as they propel us over our professional hurdles.

On a personal note, I am happily divorced after an 8-year marriage that deserves no additional words. I also made a choice to not have children early in my adulthood (though I do have a loveable, spoiled rescue dog, Morrissey, that brings me immense joy). This was a complex and highly personal decision, which I do not regret. I have immeasurable respect for women who balance raising children and their career ambitions – I simply have other interests. I love travel, have many hobbies (scuba diving, photography, gardening), and value the ability to explore my hobbies as a single woman with a very time consuming and emotionally challenging career. My loving and supportive extended family – including my parents, two incredible older brothers, two sisters-in law (both amazing professional women and mothers) – represents some of my best friends and confidants. My relationships with my closest friends plus my nieces and nephew (several which are young adults now) are critical to my happiness. As my nieces and nephews get older, I share my passion for travel with them. Ireland, Mexico, and Argentina are all countries we have already explored together!

While I don't have to defend my personal life choices, my unmarried, childless status frequently becomes part of unwelcomed conversation in my personal and professional life. Certain individuals (including acquaintances and even strangers) feel entitled to express their judgment and/or assumptions around a women's choice or ability to have children. Over the years I've learned many professional women without children also encounter these invasive questions at their workplace. I've developed several automated and brief responses to these unwelcomed and personal comments and questions. When all else fails, using strategic humor can frequently redirect or end the most awkward conversation. I've formulated reflexive brief responses to common questions and comments as an effective strategy to minimize my emotional reaction to these situations. For example, when I am mistaken for a nurse, I routinely respond with a smile, "Nursing is a wonderful profession, however, I am not a nurse. I am a physician and an orthopaedic surgeon."

Self-care is incredibly important to both happiness and professional success, however during my early years as a surgeon it wasn't a priority. Much attention is given to balancing your professional and your family's life, but there should be a third critical category – ourselves! Many busy, altruistic physicians naturally put others' needs first and their personal health and priorities can easily be marginalized. For most of my career, I struggled with back pain and sciatica and my busy life and schedule precluded me from major intervention. Subsequently chronic pain and difficulty with traditional exercise led me to gain weight and have other associated musculoskeletal issues. Fortunately, over the past five years I chose to prioritize my own health. This experience has taught me that self-care must be my single most important priority – a fact that I must frequently revisit. Physicians cannot optimally care for others (patients, parents, children, friends) if we are not healthy. Early in your career it is critical to establish and maintain a healthy living practice. During my younger years of swimming up to five hours a day, exercise naturally became my primary stress reduction tool. And it remains essential to both my physical and mental health. Regularly, I practice yoga, meditation, and mindfulness techniques as effective tools to keep both my body and mind healthy.

Mentorship has been essential to navigating my career and I have found many supportive male orthopaedic mentors. The absence of female orthopaedic mentors motivated me to reach outside my specialty and led me to my primary mentor, a professor of dermatology. Given the difference in our clinical expertise, Dr. Anne Burdick would not have naturally become my mentor. Nonetheless, unique circumstances led me to this exceptional mentor and friend, and her advice and wisdom has guided my professional and personal development. This experience has taught me to think outside of the box. If you don't see an obvious path to your goals, forge one.

Orthopaedic surgery is an amazing profession and I love my work. While my choice to become an oncologist has undoubtedly increased the emotional burden and stress level of my work, the rewards of oncology care does balance my burdens. My best days are those when I participate in curing a child with an aggressive cancer, restoring function to their leg, and watching them grow into an active healthy young adult. On my worst days, I can only hold the hand of a long-term patient who is dying despite my best surgical efforts, a great team of specialized oncologic physicians, and amazing medical and technologic advances. Fortunately, I am truly gratified by each patient encounter even in those most frustrating and sad times, when the problem exceeds the reach of the most advanced medical innovation and the surgical knife. Patients truly are physicians' greatest teachers, providing daily reminders of my role and value as a physician, beyond my role as a technical surgeon. Sometimes, even as a surgeon, being honest and compassionate is the most powerful gift we can offer.

Though workplace inequalities are real and have challenged me throughout my career, I have also seen meaningful and progressive changes in my profession. Redirecting my energy into creating positive change in my workplace is how I have responded to the inequities. I hope my specific personal challenges do not discourage, but instead, empower other women to anticipate and manage their own professional challenges. Every woman will develop her own tricks and tools to navigate her unique workplace and personal life. It is important to recognize this individuality and embrace it within ourselves and in other women. I continue to believe I've chosen a wonderful, though difficult, profession and as this field continues to diversify, it will only become a more valued and rewarding career.

In conclusion, I hope my story has value to you as you forge your unique path. Please don't forget to take care of yourself along the way, whatever that means for you! ■

Janet L. Davis, MD, MA

Leach Distinguished Professor of Ophthalmology
Bascom Palmer Eye Institute
University of Miami Miller School of Medicine

The adage that the top 10% students of medical school classes will enter academic medicine, may be true if one considers it takes drive to keep reaching for the top, even after graduating from a terminal degree program and vocational apprenticeship. In academic medicine you commit yourself to the metrics of performance in research and publication and submit to constant scrutiny and annual judgment by your chair. It is easier to count than to read, so accumulating case reports or adding single cases to a case series leads to a longer curriculum vitae but not a more substantial one, if impact is considered. A portion of my CV is papers with corporate authorship from a longstanding clinical research group in which I participate. My highest impact papers are those in which I was one of several of my retina service colleagues writing hot topic papers on age-related macular degeneration or endophthalmitis. My own work is not trivial but in a relatively obscure field. My H factor is probably higher than it should be. Nonetheless, I have just a few more peer-reviewed papers to go before I break 300 and I have written 40 book chapters.

Satisfaction from being judged worthy is likely necessary for happiness in academic medicine. Not everyone values external validation, and it is legitimate to question needing it, but not wise to ignore it unless you are self-employed. Higher education is attractive to people who *like* school and are good at it. The grade card is academic rank. The University wants you to advance and offers coaching on how to achieve higher rank. There are opportunities even if you only see patients and teach medical students. Promotion is good for you, the university, your trainees, other women who see you succeed, society, your kids, your dog – well, maybe not your dog. The most satisfying part is you chose to pursue your specialty according to your strengths. Unless you elect to go on tenure track, you can be a superannuated assistant professor and still admirably contribute to the University's mission to provide health care and train new health care workers. But you can also do more.

In my case doing more is clinical research, including investigator-sponsored projects. I gave up on lab research after an RO1 was rejected, after waiting three years without an award. I still have doubts whether practicing clinicians can perform good quality laboratory research without short-changing their patients or just seeing the easiest ones – hardly the clinical challenge one would expect an academic physician to enjoy. Sometimes you just fall into opportunities. The AIDS pandemic exploded when I first joined the faculty. Over the seven years prior to wide use of highly active anti-retroviral therapy, I became expert in the medical and surgical management of opportunistic infections of the eye. Making diagnoses by looking at spots in the back of someone's eye is the fast lane on the heuristics highway once you have enough experience. Infectious uveitis fit well with my fellowships in ocular immunology and vitreoretinal surgery. I learned a lot from my patients and my collaborative research group. After AIDS management simplified, there were new medications for use in non-infectious uveitis, new clinical research, and a new collaborative research group. I learned how to lecture and create PowerPoint presentations consisting mainly of great pictures of eye disease with a voiceover. My CV lists the over 150 national and international lectures plus several more I probably forgot to add. I have spoken all over the world – as they say, every continent but Antarctica.

Besides traveling and presenting research on behalf of subspecialty post-graduate medical education, I supported the institutional pillars of my medical specialty. The chair of my residency program told us that every year we should do something for the American Academy of Ophthalmology (AAO) and something for the American Board of Ophthalmology (ABO). AAO was easy – I have attended every year for 35 years, received recognition with a Lifetime Achievement Award and don't have to pay dues anymore. The ABO was harder. My name was proposed as a volunteer proctor for board exams and I accepted, based on direction of my chair. Ultimately, I became a board director and for one year was ABO chair and met some of the finest people in my specialty. External validation by colleagues is more pleasurable than receiving it from your employer because it is won by your effort and goes beyond your job performance. I also had the opportunity to be president of two of three uveitis subspecialty societies. My expertise in a specialty niche is an important aspect of my career. I would advise any woman, and probably any man, who wants a career in academic medicine to know quite a bit more about at least one thing than everyone else.

Each year doing well in academia gets harder, just like buying a house. Compared to the amount of information current medical students and residents must master, what I had to learn was meager. I doubt I would be a superstar today even if I could get back to my 35-year-old self. Let's assume less luck in niche selection, more competition, less personal talent. What would I do now to try to tip the balance to my side? I would learn earlier to give impeccable, timed presentations. On the other hand, I would make sure that no paper was held up under my editor's pen due to word choices. I would try to be more collaborative and break the habit of doing everything myself rather than finding someone else to do it for me. I would network more. Teamwork is the modern way to work and the only way to get enough work done. You are supposed to learn how to say "no", but I advise you to say "yes" to just about everything. Declining because you are already booked is a better excuse for tasks you would like to defer than saying no; it just takes a while to accumulate the critical mass of opportunity.

Do I recommend academics as a career? For me it was the only choice. I like medicine because I like the science, the writing, the teaching. The cognitive skills to practice are not complicated. You will be able to function as a clinician if you only care about others and communicate well and can think reasonably well. Even if you do not have these human skills, there are options for everyone. The truth is the practice of medicine can be repetitious after you have learned everything and it is supposed to be that way, because it is safer if we follow rules. It is very nice to have fresh, young, enthusiastic trainees around who are still stimulated because they haven't learned everything yet.

While waiting for someone else who can take over my job, it is very nice to have something that is as continually challenging as the academic side of medicine. Medicine, surprisingly, is a profession in which getting older does not hurt either your skills or your reputation. Experience counts, at least until decrepitude.

When I was board director and doing a lot of extra work, I used to think that without term limits I would not be able to continue. I could hold out for a certain time but if this was to be forever, then it would have to change. I have probably done too much holding on until I just really couldn't take it anymore or the task was completed. Last year I took a course in cognitive-based compassion training at Emory because I feared my growing impatience with non-compliant patients was a sign I was callous to human suffering. It turns out I was probably callous to my own suffering from too many work hours and too little reward: I'm killing myself and the patient doesn't even appreciate it enough to take their meds? Right now, I am trying to reset the balance to something easier than working 50 clinical hours and 20 academic hours each week and traveling to speak every 1-2 months. If I had invested in a practice, I would be looking for someone to buy it. As it is, I have been renting space in the house of medicine and I may be able to downsize and still have a view of the garden.

Being a doctor is a bit like being an auto mechanic. Patients are likely to agree if you tell them they need a $600 (or $6000) brake job. You can therefore be corrupted by financial reward. Working for a university helps with this moral hazard because it obscures the relationship between work and reward, i.e., it will often seem like you are working for little gain. This advantage may be lost with the new RVU-based compensation schemes and a monthly reminder of how much money you are making and where you rank compared to your colleagues. Self-supporting women need 20 times their annual salary stashed away by retirement. Ironically, this is easier when you are paid less. Even with RVUs, you may still be paid less. Women often take more time with patients, spend more time teaching, think twice before offering surgery, try to share rather than hog resources. You will be punished financially for all your best qualities. If you seek RVUs you help your employer, if you practice medicine well, you help your patients.

Everyone has a background and character and you should savor yours. In case you think I am going to tell you about a father who was a doctor, a degree from an Ivy League school, or some other predictor of success, I am not. I will tell you some things that strangely may have led me to a tenured professorship at a medical school and made me good at it.

When I discovered an undergraduate degree in English and French literature was not a sure bet for challenging employment in a recession, and a PhD in linguistics would lead to a career as a livery driver, I considered preparing for a job in which I could earn money and have job security. I wanted a professional license, so it was between law and medicine. I chose medicine because I wanted to ensure contact with all kinds of people. Perhaps that happens in law, too, with exposure to thugs and billionaire con men, but it didn't seem so at the time.

My ultra-liberal college required no science courses, but I was curious enough to take one course in "Modern Physics" and learn about Wilson cloud chambers and other cool stuff. When I finally went back to school to take the basic science prerequisites for medical school, I got the top score in organic chemistry and the best MCAT score among approximately 500 students. I interviewed in clothes I bought from a thrift store. The great state of Texas charged me only $1700 for my entire medical school tuition and my Texan husband bought groceries. When I couldn't wear jeans to work anymore, I sewed skirts from cheap material to wear on the wards. Lack of debt made it possible to undertake an additional three years of fellowship after residency.

Surprisingly my degree in English literature has come in handy. I am good at diagnosing rare eye diseases. Pattern recognition is like a plot and to a doctor, patients are semi-fictional beings. Disease, even eye disease, tells a story and if you listen to patients, they will tell you what you need to know. It doesn't happen so much anymore but asking the single Sherlockian question that reveals the diagnosis is thrilling. The degree in French has been useful as well: all the important words in Spanish are in French.

I am usually annoyed when a successful woman tries to describe her "life-work balance." I do not want to hear how to make tuna fish sandwiches for children from a woman who created a viral vector to cure congenital blindness. I know how to make sandwiches, including having someone else do it. (Actually, I know how to cook three meals per day for 30 men over six weeks because it is how I completed my master's degree in nutrition, but that is another story.) My belief is life is always in balance and people always do what they really want to do, even when it seems as if they are not. I think the balance issue is a cliché that comes up when you realize there is so much more you want to do than fits in a single life. Be happy. Have a superfluity of things you love to do and do as many as you possibly can. I congratulate any woman reading this for having or seeking a medical degree. It gives you great freedom to arrange your life as you wish, including writing and teaching.

Women asked to write their memoirs for a woman's organization may be expected to discuss their relationship to men. I deeply admire men. They form loyal friendships and are brave, kind, and generous, especially among men. Many of them truly see women as individuals and equals. Gender remains the most important social signifier although in medicine, medicine and surgical skill, knowledge, communication, and professionalism rightly dominate. Loyalty, bravery, kindness, and generosity among women will help everyone. You should support other women in medicine and ask for help from them. Get them up on the podium, out front as first authors, name them for committees. For those of you not already in the position to do this, volunteer. Until gender is considered incidental rather than defining, there is more work to be done by women, for women. Working in academic medicine can leave a trail of influence that helps both men and women grow and exceL.

Men justify leaving academic medicine for private practice as doing "what is best for their families," that is, earning a higher salary. I think there are better opportunities in academic medicine to help the multiple spheres of families to which we belong, including our sisters. I would not choose differently if I had to repeat that 1980's choice.■

Elizabeth J. Franzmann, MD

Associate Professor
Department of Otolaryngology
University of Miami Miller School of Medicine

During my early life in Sacramento, California medicine was not on my radar. My father, both grandfathers, and several uncles were pastors. This culture defined my early years. My parents generously gave their time and talents to anyone in their church who needed it. My brother and I were expected to help and as an adolescent, I was involved in service to others, entertaining children and adults. We would make meals and play with kids who lost a parent due to death, illness, or estrangement. We would visit hospital and nursing home patients to sing, play the piano, and bring homemade cookies. In that church in the 1970s and 1980s and to this day, women are not allowed to vote or take a leadership role as pastor. My parents did not subscribe to this view of women but stayed in the church throughout my childhood and young adulthood because of our strong family tradition.

Growing up, I enjoyed traditional "male" activities such as race cars, and sports just as much as I enjoyed playing with dolls and make-up. Some of the "male" interests were fostered by my only sibling, an older brother. Other interests derived from my innate need to compete and invent. I was sometimes criticized for being too "bossy" with my friends. Thankfully, my mother was able to turn a blind eye to my stained dresses, muddy shoes, and the raised eyebrows of her contemporaries and just let me do my thing. Since we were not wealthy, as I grew older, I had to work. I delivered newspapers; babysat; worked at Burger King, at a pear-packing plant, in retail; and waited tables. None of these were fulfilling jobs for me, but I did what was expected.

As a child, I intended to become a teacher like my mom and attend her alma mater, a church college. Yet I was drawn to books and articles about people suffering from disease. I would dive into *Reader's Digest* stories of miraculous recoveries from illness or trauma. In high school, my mother started asking me what I wanted to do. I thought about nursing and my mom discouraged me. She said I probably would not be satisfied taking orders and could be a doctor if I put my mind to it. I devoured a book about a woman surgeon she bought for me.

I set my sites on medical school and entered UCLA as a biology major. It is still a mystery to me why I was accepted. As I was not particularly focused on academics. I also played sports and worked. I did not have the 4.0 or near-perfect SAT scores that are required today for admission to schools like UCLA, but they were good enough.

In college, I was very focused, though a little behind some of my UCLA classmates in physics and math. When I spent hours per week working part-time jobs, my grades suffered. At times, I had to stop working and get tutoring in the subjects where I was weak. At the same time, I developed a love for science and changed my major to biochemistry. Two female mentors took me under their wing. Sandra Lamb, Ph.D. encouraged me to work in the computer lab and to push myself to graduate with College Honors by writing an undergraduate thesis and taking more challenging courses. Another mentor, Juli Feigon Ph.D., took me aside and congratulated me for achieving the highest grade in her biochemistry class. These mentors were so important to me and helped build my confidence. Another notable mentor was a famous orthopedic surgeon who discovered bone morphogenetic protein (BMP), Marshall Urist, MD. He was a surgeon-scientist who ran a fascinating lab characterizing BMP in vitro and in vivo. He was very supportive but did express concern that I had not married by the end of college.

Getting into medical school was not easy. I was initially wait listed at several schools. Toward the end of the summer after graduating from college, I was admitted to Albert Einstein. Dr. Urist spoke very highly of it, so I purchased my first wool coat and snow gear and settled in.

The school was exceptional in every way. Einstein offered an amazing education and was very accepting of me. I volunteered delivering left over food from restaurants to homeless shelters, started a student-run health clinic in the Bronx, studied, and generally led a life of service.

While I stayed out of trouble, I was homesick for my family, the sun, and the relaxed atmosphere in California. I did figure out how to study in college and did very well on my boards in my second year of medical school. In fact, now I was the one asked to tutor other students who needed help. One of my Californian friends at Albert Einstein had been able to transfer to UCLA medical school and later, I did the same.

My clinical years in medical school at UCLA were enjoyable. I chose Otolaryngology for residency having had problems with recurrent ear infections as a child. I also found the anatomy of the head and neck interesting and challenging. It would allow me the opportunity to practice oncology and develop long-term relationships with my patients.

Residency interviews were interesting. One Chairman asked if I planned to marry, whether I was going to have kids, and if so, in what order. At another institution, an older interviewer scrutinized my face and "recognized" and pointed out an asymmetry that I had never noticed. He commented that perhaps this was due to an underlying neurological condition. Strangely enough, 25 years later the neurological condition hasn't wielded its ugly head! Thankfully, I did not wind up at either of those institutions.

Medical school graduation was an exciting event with friends and family coming from all over the country. There had never been a physician on either side of my family. My very conservative paternal grandfather was the loudest cheerleader in the quad when my name was called.

I arrived at the University of Miami for residency a couple of years after Hurricane Andrew. Most people were still shell-shocked. They would tell stories of roofs flying off, huddling under mattresses, etc. While I had listened to the news, the reality of hurricanes and South Florida culture did not hit me until I was living it. This time around, a few years older and in often sunny Florida, I was able to adjust to all the cultural and weather differences.

I was the second female resident in our program. The first graduated before I started. There had been a female pediatric otolaryngology attending, but she left prior to my arrival. Donna Lundy, our esteemed speech pathologist, is the only female faculty that is still with our department from that time. There were hiccups as the all-male surgeons and trainees in the Otolaryngology Department did their best to make me feel welcome. But, for the most part, they were professional and excellent teachers. I had a particularly wonderful mentor in Dr. Jerry Goodwin. He helped foster my interest in research on CD44, facilitated Ph.D. mentors, and helped me successfully compete for local and a national resident research award. I also competed, though unsuccessfully, for several small grants during this period.

Unbeknownst to him, Jerry Goodwin also played a key role in introducing me to my husband. Back in the old days, you often did not sleep when you were on call and then worked a full day into the next evening. The day I met my future husband was no different. I had a sleepless call night and had already worked many hours into the next day's schedule. Jerry Goodwin called for an extra pair of hands to help him retract. I was struggling to stay awake and Dr. Goodwin was getting annoyed. In the background was a very jovial anesthesiology fellow, cracking jokes. After the case, a train of nurses followed me into the changing room to tell me, "Dr. Deo is going to ask you out!" When you are looking for love, people always tell you it happens when you least expect it. This was 100% true in my case. I responded, "Who is Dr. Deo?" To the nurses' amazement and my own, I had somehow missed this eligible bachelor. I paid much closer attention the next time I was called to cover Sylvester Comprehensive Cancer Center.

My surgical residency years were amazing and exhausting. One night during internship I was up late taking care of my scut list and putting out fires. My young teenage patient, one of the first to have a laparoscopic cholecystectomy, had still not been seen. The attending emphasized this patient must be reminded to perform incentive spirometry. I walked in her room around midnight focused on cajoling the teenager into deep breathing. She and her relatives were, of course, sleeping. I woke her up or tried to without success. She looked at me and her eyes rolled back. She was breathing, had a pulse, and was sort of arousable. I ordered some labs and called my chief resident describing what happened. She immediately instructed me to get a hemoglobin level and prepare the patient for the operating room. She had bled into the abdomen and her hemoglobin was dangerously low. Fortunately, the chief resident and attending stopped the bleeding. The patient would have died if I had waited until morning to remind her to breathe into the spirometer.

My most effectual surgical mentors were the ones who encouraged a "you can do it" attitude. Negative re-enforcement reminded me that no one in my family had ever been a doctor and fostered self-questioning. The first emergency chest tube, tracheotomy, solo parotidectomy, and solo laryngectomy were milestones that taught me important lessons. Mistakes happened, though rarely. The saying that helped me the most during this time was from Dr. Goodwin. "Mistakes happen, but it is what you do about them that matters." We must learn from our mistakes and develop corrective and preventative action plans.

John and I married in a special ceremony, led by my father. Many of our colleagues were there to celebrate with us. I had interviewed at top Head and Neck Surgery Fellowships across the country but decided to stay in Miami for personal reasons and to continue my research on CD44. Besides, UM had, and still has, one of the strongest Head and Neck clinical programs in the country.

Fellowship was not without drama. Dr. Goodwin had stepped down as chairman and was focused on the cancer center. Usually, a fellow in my position would be looking for their first full-time job at the National Meeting that was scheduled for September 2001. While the plan was that I would join the faculty, our new chairman created an obstacle, late in the process – he would hire me only if I secured peer-reviewed, grant support. Previously there was no similar pre-requisite for hiring faculty in our department. On September 11, 2001, as our world was turning upside down with the toppling of the Twin Towers, I was feverishly trying to submit the grant application on which my entire career was dependent. I was awarded a Young Investigator Award from the Flight Attendant Medical Research Institute (FAMRI) and along with the cancer center support, joined the faculty in 2002, shortly after Giovana Thomas who was hired the previous year. On my first attempt, I successfully established NIH R03 funding in my second year. This led to an incorrect assumption that achieving further NIH funding would be easy. Quickly, reality set in as an R01 proved harder to achieve. My first submission was scored but did not receive a fundable score. I worked for months over weekends and vacation on the next submission and only scored a couple of points higher. Finally, in 2007, on my third attempt, I was awarded an R01 grant, five years after joining the faculty and just as my Young Investigator Award was depleted. I was the first R01-funded surgeon-scientist on faculty in our department and was promoted in 2008 to Associate Professor.

In the meantime, in 2003 and 2006 we welcomed our daughters into the world. We quickly learned about nannies, housekeepers, and the complexities of household management. My husband, who also works full-time helps at home, otherwise my work would be impossible. I did then, and still, work nights and weekends to get things done. He has been endlessly supportive and very involved in our children's sports and academics. His parents also helped, when they were alive, and my parents also recently moved to Miami to help too.

After the initial promotion, I started to notice something strange. While the R01 was supposed to be the holy grail of academics and the key to unfettered success for a surgeon-scientist, it seemed like my NIH R01 and I were becoming invisible. Research demands took up much of my nights and weekends. I was also spending many extra hours taking junior residents through complex patient care in the clinic and operating room at JMH. Few attendings had time to train junior residents who did not know how to operate yet. At the same time, financial support at JMH was limited in terms of personnel, administrative assistance, and salary support.

Soon, male junior faculty that I helped train would be given leadership positions. On the bright side, we were admitting more and more talented female residents and fellows into our program. Yet the department leadership, particularly surgical leadership, did not reflect the changing times. The annual end of year Chandler research program and graduation celebration was emblematic of this. The festivities were led every year by a peculiarly all-male parade. Men organized and ran the Chandler program. Men represented the department and each division as awards and diplomas were given to the trainees. Men acknowledged each other for years of service and gave each other Chair Awards. As a woman I felt invisible. I also noticed that it was not just me who was invisible. Other very accomplished, innovative female faculty also seemed to have this invisibility superpower. Slowly, I stopped going to department events.

By 2010, my research on CD44 was translated into a diagnostic test. I was successfully completing enrollment into a National Cancer Institute-funded case-control trial. Early on I submitted a renewal that was triaged. At that time, it was a challenge to get funding through NCI for development work, the test needed prior to running a pivotal trial also required by the study section. Rather than renew the R01 in 2010, I began focusing the lab on a Bankhead-Coley grant, similar in scope to an R01, investigating the early detection test to minimize disparities in oral cancer. We were also generating strong research related to CD44 as a target for therapy funded through other peer-reviewed mechanisms. This period of growth required financial support. The Chair position again changed hands to Dr. Telischi. From the beginning he saw my potential, and as the Chair invested in my laboratory. This came at a critical time as the cancer center, also under new leadership, was cutting the apron strings.

UM Innovation has also been very supportive of my work from the beginning and to this day. In 2010, with the patent prospects looking strong, UM Innovation, led by Norma Kenyon, Ph.D., introduced me to a patent lawyer and entrepreneur, Matthew Kim. A short time later in 2011, Vigilant Biosciences was founded based on UM's intellectual property – a simple, inexpensive, noninvasive oral cancer early detection test. I volunteered to do my initial research with Vigilant since the start-up company's funding was exceedingly tight. Soon afterwards the initial patents were granted.

I struggled to engage leaders of the Cancer Center, Otolaryngology Department and Head and Neck Division with my research and vision for an affordable, noninvasive oral cancer early detection test. However, they were spread thin struggling to garner resources and finances to sustain their research and vision. In contrast, Vigilant Biosciences aggressively pursued my expertise. I was afraid of going to the "dark side" with industry and still felt an attachment to my colleagues in the head and neck division. I offered myself for a leadership position at UM in the Division of Head and Neck Research. My chairman provided the title, but it did not come with staff support or backing from the Cancer Center. Lacking synergy with colleagues and financial support, it was not the correct fit.

As Vigilant's funding position strengthened, the company offered me the Chief Scientific Officer position, which I accepted. This was a turning point for me. I started to grasp an important concept: translating research into products that add value to our patients could make research fiscally sustainable. Experience taught me that NIH funding does not cover the costs of the research that is proposed. While prestigious, NIH funding comes at a high price for the institution. The University has a win-win policy when it comes to intellectual property. The proceeds are divided into thirds that go to the inventors, department, and the University.

In this role, I helped the company develop a point-of care version of the CD44 and total protein early detection test for oral and oropharyngeal cancer. Around the same time, Vigilant began supporting my laboratory through a contract with UM. This provided the support I needed to build synergistic relationships. The point-of care-test was launched in Europe primarily in research trials in Denmark, Germany, and Italy. Others would soon begin in India and New Zealand. The pivotal FDA study for the point of care product began in 2017 and is still ongoing. To date, this team effort has resulted in over

$6 million dollars in peer-reviewed funding, $25 million in investor funding for Vigilant, over 50 peer-reviewed publications, and 24 US and International patents.

I am grateful to the mentors who have helped me along the way. I am thankful for friends who understand my crazy hours and put up with my intensity. My female colleagues and trainees, who understand the struggle of being a woman in a traditionally male-dominated field, are an endless source of inspiration and encouragement. I am thankful for the patients who move me with both vulnerability and strength. They make me want to be a better doctor, scientist, and person. Most importantly, I am grateful for my family who loves me, forgives me, makes me laugh, and makes life wonderful. ■

Lilian M. Abbo, MD, FIDSA

Chief Infection Prevention & Antimicrobial Stewardship
Jackson Health System
Professor of Infectious Diseases
Department of Medicine & Miami Transplant Institute
University of Miami Miller School of Medicine

I was born in Philadelphia, PA while my father was training in physical medicine and rehabilitation and my mom was graduating in economics at the University of Pennsylvania. When I was three months old, we moved back to Caracas, Venezuela and I lived there most of my life until July of 2000 when I emigrated back to the U.S. As the oldest of three siblings, I have two terrific brothers (both engineers). My maternal grandparents were Holocaust survivors from Romania and my paternal grandparents were born in Safed, Israel but moved to Venezuela and Panama in the 1930s.

Growing up in Venezuela was a fantastic experience. My family is comprised of a large clan and any celebration or family illness may rally at least 400 people ready to help and support each other. I went to the same school from pre-K to high school and was very close to my childhood friends. At 16, I graduated from high school committed to conquering injustice in the world. My mom advised me to pick a career I would love doing for the rest of my life, one I could practice anywhere in the world if we had to emigrate ("as Jews you never know"), and that offered financial independence. My dad always thought I was going to be a lawyer. When I chose medicine, he said I would see my friends and siblings graduate sooner than me and make more money than I would ever see but "in medicine you will have more personal satisfaction than any of your peers; a patient's gratitude is priceless." Both pieces of advice were correct.

In Venezuela, from very early in my medical school career I was exposed to a sisterhood of smart, talented, funny, and supportive friends who have all inspired me to be a better doctor and person. Medical school also exposed me to the crude reality of practicing medicine in a developing country where resources are extremely limited. A good medical history and your clinical skills (sometimes just a stethoscope and a flashlight) are often your only and most valuable tools. We had to make complex diagnoses and provide care to the very poor and critically ill with limited technology and sometimes we paid out of our pocket for our patients' medications. Some of the issues that inspired me to pursue a career in infectious disease included preventative care campaigns to educate patients about the benefits of good hygiene and dehydration prevention (when most children died from diarrhea and had limited access to potable water), planned parenthood to limit adolescent pregnancies and the spread of HIV, and free immunization programs.

I met my husband during my last year of medical school. We moved to Miami to pursue my residency and fellowship with plans to return home. However, life had other plans for us and due to the political situation in Venezuela we never went back. We have two amazing children, Veronica and Joseph, who are my heroes and inspire me to be a better person every day.

I graduated from the Universidad Central de Venezuela and subsequently completed an internship in Jacobi Medical Center (Yeshiva University) in the Bronx, NY; residency in internal medicine at Mount Sinai Medical Center (Miami Beach); and fellowship in infectious disease at Jackson Memorial Hospital/UM. In Miami, for about 8 months I was in private practice and then returned to UM/Jackson where I have been a faculty member since 2008. During my fellowship I fell in love with the field of transplantation and gravitated toward the care of the most complex patients with serious infections. It is an honor to be part of a team that creates miracles daily.

The title of a new book by Dr. J. Mezrich, *When Death Becomes Life* is very meaningful to me. In organ donation, we largely depend on deceased donors who unexpectedly pass away. Their families are faced with the option of giving their organs to maintain their legacy. Thanks to that non-reciprocal gift we can give the gift of life to thousands of patients who otherwise would have no hope. As I started my journey in the growing field of transplant infectious disease, Jackson Memorial Hospital offered me the position of medical director for the Antimicrobial Stewardship Program (ASP). I had to learn on the job and was blessed to have an amazing partner and friend as our stewardship pharmacist. For the next 10 years Laura Smith, PharmD and I worked tirelessly to revamp and expand the appropriate use of antibiotics across the health system. I had wonderful mentors, both physicians and pharmacists, who helped me along the way. Starting in this field was innovative and challenging. With our talented colleagues, we had to figure out how to care for critically ill, immunocompromised patients in our under-resourced system. Some of my mentors included colleagues at other institutions and countries who were either more experienced or at that time just starting their programs like we were. I learned that being open and reaching out to people I didn't know was extremely important. Most people in infectious disease are willing to help if you ask, even if they have never heard of you. I also learned to pay it forward and try to help students, residents, researchers, and clinicians whenever they reach out from all over the world.

Currently, I serve Jackson Health System, one of the country's largest public safety-net hospital systems, as the Chief for Infection Prevention and Antimicrobial Stewardship and work with a terrific and diverse team of infection preventionists and clinical pharmacists. In my role I have direct responsibility and authority for strategic assessment and implementation of programs to prevent and control healthcare-associated infections, the appropriate use of antibiotics, and I work closely with our microbiology laboratory. I am core faculty at the Miami Transplant Institute and am involved in the selection of patients, organ donors, and management of complex immunocompromised patients with multidrug resistant infections. I am also principal investigator in several grants related to antimicrobial resistance.

Nationally, I serve on several committees for the Infectious Disease Society of America and as a board member of the American Society of Transplantation Infectious Disease Community of Practice. Some of my professional development activities have included: Certificate in Executive Healthcare Leadership (Cornell University), Michael Porter's Value Based Healthcare Intensive Seminar (Harvard Business School), AAMC Mid-Career Leadership Development, and Green Belt Six Sigma certification (UM). In the past I served the UM Health System as the Associate Chief for Patient Safety and Quality. Between 2014-2017 I served as UMMSM President of Women in Academic Medicine (WIAM). This was a truly enriching opportunity to serve our institution and foster peer to peer mentoring, promotion, personal and professional development, and work closely with faculty members from other departments and other schools within UM. I worked with a terrific group of women from the Office of Diversity including Nanette Vega and with my faculty peers, members of the WIAM board. Mentoring and sponsorships go beyond our own divisions or departments. Holding the ladder and helping others to move up is very important. I value having great mentors and being able to mentor some terrific students, residents, fellows, and my own team members to advance their careers and juggle our multiple personal and professional responsibilities. Expanding the mentoring, sponsorship, and leadership skills of our faculty is important to me. I believe diversity and inclusion are core values for a strong university. Equal pay and equal opportunities for promotion are important and need to be prioritized early in our careers.

I am driven by a strong passion and desire to help our patients. I believe it is truly an honor and privilege to practice medicine every day of my life. Caring for people in the most difficult moments of their lives and providing high quality care to everyone regardless of their ability to pay, is what drives me to make our hospitals a better and safer place.

As a strong supporter of life and work balance or "juggle," my favorite past-times are long walks on the beach, reading, and traveling around the world. I exercise daily and love Zumba, boxing, and yoga. Working out helps keep me sane and reminds me to be grateful for everything we have and for what we won't have in our lives. ■

Viviana Elizabeth Horigian, MD, MHA

Associate Professor
Director of Public Health Education
University of Miami Miller School of Medicine

My passion for teaching public health stems from my belief and commitment to empowering others to achieve growth, learning, and change by capacity building and increased self-sufficiency. Over my career, I have fulfilled and exceeded my commitment by working with individuals, families, communities, and large health systems. I seized opportunities for capacity building and developed internationally and nationally recognized applied research education projects.

As the granddaughter of four Armenian genocide survivors my awareness of their traumatic history truly shaped my dedication, perseverance, and resiliency. My grandparents' life experiences taught me that under no circumstances, was I ever to give up. I also learned change and growth is possible when provided with knowledge, tools, and opportunity. My career is dedicated to facilitating growth and success.

I was born and raised in Buenos Aires, Argentina and when I decided to apply to medical school it was unusual for a woman raised in our Armenian culture to pursue a career in medicine. Instead the cultural expectations were to marry, stay home, and raise children. Fortunately, my father supported my dream to become a doctor and I was trained as a psychiatrist in Buenos Aires. During my residency training my motivation was fueled for studying psychiatry by witnessing the psychological pain of patients at home visits. Then I was selected as the chief resident and later as instructor of residents in psychiatry at the Hospital Italiano de Buenos Aires. My role was to engage residents and faculty in a participatory process to update the curriculum and transform the learning experience to make it more relevant and applicable in their practice, while respecting the academic requirements. I also created new opportunities for direct coaching and mentorship to develop first year residents' clinical skills. My goal was to bring about change and improve their learning experience. In recognition of my contributions, simultaneously I was re-elected for a second term and appointed clinical assistant professor in psychiatry for students at the Universidad de Buenos Aires Medical School. As a resident instructor, I taught two courses, *Therapeutic Attitude and Advances in Psychiatry*, for first- and third-year residents respectively, and established a weekly research workshop for all residents. Since then I've focused on teaching research methods to clinicians so they may develop a better understanding of the critical role research plays in advancing health practices. I have relied on the use of practical research projects as a method of developing experiential learning coursework so clinicians can develop research competencies.

The weekly residents' research workshop resulted in the first research study conducted by psychiatry residents at the Hospital Italiano de Buenos Aires. The study measured the comorbidity of personality disorders and panic attacks among the hospital's emergency room patients. My department colleagues were doubtful we would be able to conduct research that relied on prospective real time data collection, particularly in the emergency department. I conducted training on the administration of standardized measures and data collection procedures. Weekly I met with the residents to review new cases and ensure standardization in the implementation of study procedures. For residents and faculty, the research conducted in real-time emphasized the importance of structured research methods. We presented our research at the 1998 American Psychiatric Association annual meeting. In addition, under my mentorship, two additional research studies resulted from the research workshop and were presented at the 1999 World Psychiatric Association meeting. This was the first time Hospital Italiano de Buenos Aires psychiatry residents presented research at international conferences.

While leading the residents' training program one of the challenges I addressed was providing access for psychiatry residents to learn from research results published in English. Since the residents' English language reading skills were very limited, I was hired by Editorial Panamericana in Buenos Aires to translate *Psychodynamic Psychiatry in Clinical Practice*, a core textbook for residents by Dr. Glenn Gabbard. My specific interest in the book was the integrative approach presented to understand treatment of mental illness. With Gabbard's support, the content provided a way to address the polarization among psychoanalytic and biologically-oriented psychiatric practice, and for many years this book was used in the residency program.

My interest in creating structures and opportunities for research within the department for future generations was realized when my colleague, the Department of Psychiatry Chair, and I co-founded the Psychiatry Center for Clinical Research at the Hospital Italiano de Buenos Aires. Soon after the Center was designated a clinical research site for the FDA-regulated and pharmaceutical industry funded multi-site phase II and III trials. It wasn't easy to develop the Center and then roll out studies. Although my colleagues thought it was an important milestone, they were doubtful such a center would ever be sustainable. Building on the resident research workshop and establishing the Center for Clinical Research solidified the importance and central role of systematic, rigorous research with the international and national publication of research results which continues to flourish. While in Buenos Aires, I conducted research, had a hospital appointment, and saw private practice patients. Following my interest in the dynamics of couples and families, I completed post-graduate studies in couples and family therapy.

My passion for complex behavioral intervention clinical trials brought me to the U.S. where I joined the University of Miami (UM) Center for Family Studies. I coordinated a multi-site, randomized effectiveness trial on Brief Strategic Family Therapy (BSFT) for adolescent drug abuse. The BSFT effectiveness study was one of the largest adolescent family therapy trials ever conducted. This bilingual (English-Spanish) study was conducted within the NIH/National Institute on Drug Abuse (NIDA) National Drug Abuse Treatment Clinical Trials Network (CTN), a partnership between scientists and community treatment providers to develop, validate, and implement practical, innovative, and relevant clinical trials in diverse community settings. Ultimately the goal of CTN is to bridge the gap between research and practice, using science to facilitate the adoption of evidence-based interventions for substance abuse treatment. This network strengthens and develops the workforce for substance abuse treatment by training community-based teams to conduct randomized clinical trials, and by disseminating study results. In my role as national study coordinator for the BSFT multi-site effectiveness trial, I established structures and systems to implement the trial in accordance with FDA standards and developed training. At that time BSFT protocol training differed from others in the network because it provided specific hands-on opportunities, and it established a system to determine competence through observation of pilot cases by senior trained staff. This became a requirement for endorsing study staff to begin the research activities. I developed the criteria to evaluate competence in all areas of protocol implementation. And from 2004-2008, I established weekly calls for research assistants to review study procedures and used this forum to provide mentoring and re-training nationwide to 24 research assistants.

Behavioral interventions such as BSFT could pose challenges in defining the safety plan for the trial because the standard procedures for safety monitoring are based on pharmacological and device intervention trials, which are often based on observed physical signs and symptoms. In response I worked with the NIDA CTN medical monitor and the BSFT lead investigator to develop a safety plan appropriate and relevant to family therapy intervention. I trained researchers and practitioners on the importance of safety monitoring and the specifics for the BSFT trial. In 2010 I published my research in the journal, *Clinical Trials*, in an article titled *Principles for defining adverse events in behavioral intervention research: Lessons from a family focused adolescent drug abuse trial*. The publication provides behavioral intervention researchers guiding principles to elaborate on an appropriate safety plan for the interventions being tested and allows practitioners to understand the importance of identification and safety monitoring. Due to industry recognition of my work on safety issues, I was invited to serve as a member of five data safety monitoring boards for behavioral intervention trials.

And in 2007, I was appointed director and in 2013, executive director of the UM-based clinical trials center on drug abuse treatment. The UM center is one of the 13 NIH/NIDA-funded clinical trials centers of the National Drug Abuse Treatment Clinical Trial Network, and I was charged with overseeing the administrative operations. The areas I became responsible for included the operational areas such as quality assurance, data management, medical monitoring, biostatistics, project management, training, and dissemination. During my 11-year tenure I grew the network and the UM center was highly productive. Under my academic leadership the UM center was awarded three one-year scholar grants to mentor young national and international scientists on the implementation of randomized clinical trials in real world settings. In addition, at the provider level my leadership directly impacted training and development as reflected by the growth. Several providers established their own research centers at community-based treatment programs, including the Cowdery Addictions Research Institute at Gateway Community Services in Jacksonville Florida, and the Research Center at Operation PAR in Tampa/St. Petersburg Florida. Now, both research centers successfully compete for federal grants.

Since 2012, I have taught the *Clinical Trials* (EPH 604) course to students pursuing their Master's in Public Health (MPH) degree at UM's Department of Public Health Sciences (DPHS), and in UM's PhD programs in epidemiology, prevention, and biostatistics. And I also advised more than 40 MPH and MD/MPH students in the *Capstone Field Experience* (EPH 680) and the *Capstone project* (EPH 681) courses, which together form the Capstone Experience, a vital component of the MPH program. The Capstone Field Experience provides students with real-world work experience in the field of public health. Students placed in health-related settings (local, national, and international) work on projects of mutual interest to both the field organization and the student. The Capstone Project is geared toward building upon this fieldwork and the student can apply public health academic theory and acquired skills to community health problems. In 2014, I was appointed to lead the 21st Century innovation of the Capstone Experience by creating an 18-month-long MPH Learning Collaboratory, instead of a one-time experience. By creating the Learning Collaboratory the learning experience of MPH students was transformed by providing opportunities to develop core skills for effective public health practice.

My commitment to teaching goes beyond borders and extends across systems. In March 2011, the U.S Department of State awarded me with a training grant to transfer the technology used by UM's NIH/NIDA-funded National Drug Abuse Treatment Clinical Trials Network Center to Mexico's National Institutes of Psychiatry. This initiative provided me with the opportunity to develop an innovative mentoring program. I mentored researchers at the National Institute of Psychiatry to develop research infrastructure and implement a network to conduct randomized clinical trials in real world settings to test the effectiveness of treatments for substance abuse and mental health problems.

I used science to change Mexico's treatment on the frontline of their practice. In the process I developed a model for transnational technology transfer to create research networks and run rigorous randomized clinical trials. This included delivering training and most importantly experiential learning through implementing the network and conducting its first randomized clinical trial including mentorship. Ultimately the goal was to help train academic researchers who could implement rigorous randomized clinical trials in real world settings through collaborations with community partners and train-the-trainers on evidence-based practices and publish their results. I remember when proposing the project many of my colleagues questioned its feasibility. Some of them cautioned it may detour my career. I thought otherwise, and now I can say it was one of my best life experiences. I trained researchers and post docs and they were successful in developing research leading to practice collaboration, implementing rigorous trials, and trainers in their own country. The seminal paper describing our methodology is titled, *Technology Transfer for the Implementation of a Clinical Trials Network on Drug Abuse and Mental Health in Mexico* published in the *Panamerican Health Organization* journal. Under my leadership, the UM team coached the Mexican Institute of Psychiatry to create a Clinical Trials Unit (Unidad de Ensayos Clínicos, UEC). Notably, the Clinical Trials Unit was successful in launching, implementing and completing the first randomized trial implemented in the network with the quality and rigor of trials implemented in the U.S. Since the network launch, it has expanded to include 43 new treatment centers participating in research, improved research capacity through training at the treatment centers, delivered evidence-based interventions and disseminated results. In 2010, the Mexican Narcotics Affairs Division formally recognized the Mexico Technology Transfer Project again in 2013, during the closing ceremony of the first clinical trial, the project was awarded for our "invaluable contribution and collaboration towards the development of the Mexican National Clinical Trials Network." In 2017, Dr Navarrete and I were invited to teach a course in clinical trials for addiction and mental health treatment at the Institute of Psychiatry in Mexico. Following its initial success, we were invited to expand this course to a full week boot camp in 2018.

In June 2015 not only was I promoted to Associate Professor on the educator tenure track but I was also recognized by the National Institute Drug Abuse with an award of excellence in international leadership for developing international collaborative research and capacity building. The technology transfer model I developed and two projects on which I served as adviser were implemented at the la Universidad Católica Santiago de Guayaquil (CSG) in Ecuador, and la Fundación San Carlos de Maipo in Chile for the Familias Unidas project to prevent adolescent substance abuse. The innovative model of technology transfer continues to serve as the guiding principle of the work of the DPHS as I lead the Department's initiatives in the Americas.

On January 2016, I was appointed Interim Director for Public Health Education in the DPHS and offered this position permanently in 2018. I oversee the programmatic and administrative aspects of the MPH and MSPH programs. I developed a strategic plan centered on four major goals to attract the best students, enhance their learning experience, enrich the teaching experience for faculty, and improve systems and quality outcomes of our educational programs. With the goal of improving the students' educational experience, we began comprehensive advising, so students start working on day one with a faculty member to delineate their choices and pace of coursework, including identifying the field experience and choosing their area of interest and future career path. I also began offering student-led panels on critical topics in public health to promote student advocacy and facilitate collaborations and exchange with faculty and community partners.

As an educator, I wholeheartedly believe in lifelong learning and its importance in making us better educators. In 2017, I decided to pursue an online Master's in Health Administration degree to gain formal training in aspects of public health, management and health administration. I wanted to have a better understanding of healthcare service delivery. A desire to experience the student's online learning environment drove me to pursue this degree late in life so I can develop and offer DPHS online courses.

In May 2018 my passion for capacity building and training in drug abuse treatment led me to pursue a grant, in collaboration with my colleagues, to present an inaugural Miami conference on opioid treatment. While dedicating my career to capacity building regarding drug abuse treatment and now to the opioid epidemic, I was invited to develop training modules for evidence-based treatment of opioid use disorders for providers in community settings and to deliver training.

Throughout my career, I remained committed to creative instructional development tied to research. By working hard to attain my goal to become an outstanding teacher and adviser I have earned an international reputation. I challenged existing systems with innovative strategies that allowed structures to develop and facilitate international and national capacity building to conduct research. Globally, I am committed to improving public health in underdeveloped societies and intend to continue my work toward building capacities to improve practice, as I already have in the Americas. I was able to realize my full potential by listening to my heart, sticking to my values, remaining centered in my purpose, and never forgetting where my journey began. ■

Stefanie Brown, MD, FACP, FAAP

Program Director, Internal Medicine
Section Chief – Med-Peds
Section Chief – Pediatric Hospital Medicine
Assistant Professor of Medicine and Pediatrics
University of Miami Miller School of Medicine

My earliest memories of my desire to be a physician emanated from watching a TV show on ABC from 1969 to 1976 titled, *Marcus Welby MD*. The show presented the daily life of a general practitioner in a small town who saw patients in the office, made house calls, and saw entire families over many years. As I watched the show I thought, that is what I want to do, I want to be a doctor!

My friends and colleagues know me as someone who is always practical, organized, and driven. I love lists, white boards, and a good spreadsheet makes my day. Personally, I live by two sets of rules, the first set I use in my medical practice which I share with my teams on their first day of rounds during an "expectations setting" conversation. And the second set I use for dating, which I won't share now. I will share my rules as a story with the lessons I learned and reflect upon how each tied to a pivotal point in my career. And my story begins with the intro lesson.

Lesson #1
Practicing medicine is different than portrayed on 1970's television.
Rule #1
You are not your grades.

In high school I was a straight A student, and mainly an A student in college. I was valued more for my brain power than for my style or engaging personality as an awkward yet happily introverted nerd. I spent most of my time with my nose in books (fiction and non-fiction), and still consider my library card my most valuable asset. Like many eager young medical students before me, having easily achieved academic success up to this point, I had a rude awakening in medical school. I learned I was just average and sometimes even below average (gasp!). If I wasn't the smart one, what was I? I struggled with this as I perceived my entire identity up to this point as based only on my academic achievement. It took my entire preclinical years to realize as a physician and an adult, life was more than grades. I began a journey of self-discovery to focus on my positive attributes and not just the good grades. I began to explore my conscious and subconscious so I could express my thoughts, my values and natural abilities, and wish to serve humanity. And I began to blossom beyond the awkward introverted nerd. I was just getting started and after repeatedly questioning my choices and decisions I've arrived at this point in my life.

Lesson #2

Do the work to find yourself as soon as you believe you are lost.

    Rule # 2

    "Haters going to hate" – aka the Taylor Swift rule.

During my first third-year medical school clerkship I was paired with an intern named Howard Sobel and we began our study of internal medicine. Howard was incredibly smart, clinically savvy, compassionate, caring, and seemed to be very knowledgeable about everything. I found myself thinking, "I want to be that guy" (another Marcus Welby moment). Howard asked me which area in the study of medicine I wanted to pursue and I replied, family medicine. He asked me why and I said, I want to take care of entire families, adults and children. I wanted to see patients in the hospital, or an office or in their home. He suggested Internal Medicine-Pediatrics or Med-Peds. Med-Peds is a specialty requiring four years of training, two years in both pediatrics and Internal Medicine. Upon graduation you attain board-certification in both specialties. As Howard explained this it fit with my perceptions of 1970's medicine. The show portrayed the complex medical situations the TV doctor faced every day and Dr. Welby was agile and flexible and never bored. Officially I began to pursue my career in Med-Peds. I started hanging out with Med-Peds residents, going to conferences, asking questions, and soon I realized I found my family, my home, my people, and my vocation.

I met with my advising dean and said I wanted to go into Med-Peds practice and the "hateration" began. If you're not familiar with that word the urban dictionary defines "hateration" as negative emotion and energy directed at others. When a medical student announces their intention to practice Med-Peds the "hateration" is directed at them in an outpouring of what I refer to as "Med-Peds Urban Legends" or "Myths of Med-Peds." In the eyes of others, our choice makes us a unicorn, beautiful and magical, and most people don't believe we exist… do not be dissuaded by the legends or the myths. The "hateration" usually begins as a rant something like this:

"OMG, why do you want to do that? – It's an extra year. It's too competitive. Why don't you just practice family medicine, you can't learn both specialties in four years and what are you going to do with it? What's the point when you will just end up doing one or the other?"

Some medical school deans still believe this to be true. In response, I took a deep breath and channeled my inner Gandhi, Martin Luther King, Jr. and other non-violent historical figures. As I considered it a teachable moment, I chose to respond with data defending my choices.

Lesson #3

The "Haters going to hate," but don't get angry, get data.

- And as Taylor Swift says, "Shake it off."

    Rule #3

    Make it happen.

I applied to Med-Peds or MP as my only specialty and successfully matched. At the time, the programs were co-directed by the Medicine program director (PD) and the Peds PD. I was granted my requested schedule and began on Peds and during my third month of Peds, I got a call from the Medicine PD. A colleague was sick or pregnant and my schedule had to be changed. My first month in medicine, supposedly an elective, became a month in the ICU. Subsequently this occurred more often and when I finished residency, I completed nine months in adult ICU which was categorized by the medicine program as "wards or subspecialty exposure," mainly due to minimal attention. At the time, the ACGME was not accrediting combined programs instead they were administered by the respective boards. By the end of my PGY-3 year, I was assigned an unbalanced curriculum in which Med-Peds was last on the list of the program directors, as it wasn't their "real" job.

During my PGY-4 year, I was asked to be a PGY-5 Medicine Primary Care chief resident. I tried to take advantage of this "pre-leadership" period to lead so no other students suffered. This was one of my first administrative decision-making moments. I volunteered to do the master schedule for the Med-Peds residents and requested any changes from both sides to meet ACGME requirements. I achieved success and eliminated the nine-month ICU schedule.

Historically the Medicine program led coordinating the Med-Peds recruitment interview schedule with the Peds department. I volunteered to coordinate and host all recruitment after Medicine and Peds decided on the dates. I'm proud of the success achieved - a formal Med-Peds interview day hosted by Med-Peds residents and faculty.

Lesson #4

Get creative and take every opportunity to "make it happen." – *Often you can work with people in a "come with me" approach. When you can't, you may have to go around them, under them, over them, and as a last resort, through them. Under the right circumstances, it is better to ask for forgiveness than permission.*

Rule #4
Say no as often as you need to say it.

I joined the Med-Peds faculty after my year as chief where I did 100% clinical work and spent half my time teaching in resident clinics. I toiled along, happy and oblivious in my Med-Peds world. I believe the difficulty of working in Med-Peds is that many of us enjoy using our problem-solving capacity all the time. I believe students who are attracted to Med-Peds love and thrive on challenge and use nature and nurture to maintain their "make it happen" attitude. Early in my career I never said "no" to any requests because, "That's the Med-Peds way." I never questioned my ability to implement any request and just figured I would learn along the way. In retrospect, this was a double-edged sword.

From 2001-2007, I began my professional medical career and worked for two years as Associate Program Director for ambulatory education. From the start I didn't ask for guidance from the PD. I made the schedule and ensured we had adequate preceptor coverage. Two years later, in 2004 when I was appointed Associate Dean for Evaluation it wasn't clear then, or now, why I was chosen for the job. The position was my first encounter with structured mentorship and faculty development for those seeking an academic career. For the first time, I started to formally plan my academic medical career and seek the training I needed. Beginning in 2002, 2004, and again in 2006, I served as interim medical director for the department of Medicine faculty practice. It wasn't until my third time in the role that I requested funding to take a faculty practice boot camp course and learned about performance expectations. Looking back, saying yes to all the professional roles proved to be an incredible learning experience. For example, I learned about leadership, I found real mentorship and was exposed to practice management and hospital administration. This experience reminded me of my first time working as a resident in the ICU – terrifying but fun learning daily on the job. Saying "yes" to any and all that was requested of me was detrimental because at the end of seven years, I was burnt out and hated medicine. I was not strategic about the requests to which I said yes, and I did not advance my own goals with many of these opportunities. I served others without ever thinking about how to reach my own goals.

Lesson #5
Say yes but think strategically – *"That's the Med-Peds way."*
(Please insert your specialty here) – this is a universal rule for all faculty.

Rule #5
Never say die.

While reviewing the advice shared under rule #4, I realized in addition to education and clinical care, I enjoyed administration. When I decided to pursue the role of Med-Peds program director, I had already been leading the program for six years. The areas included curriculum development, clinic administration, Med-Peds ambulatory education, etc. and I was working without the protected time or the title. In 2007, ACGME took over the Med-Peds program oversight. I spoke with the co-directors of our Med-Peds program at the time and shared my interest in the position as a combined program director, as recommended by the ACGME. They responded that I would have to pry it out of their cold dead hands. Their response forced me to do one of the hardest things I have ever done, after 11 years I left the place I called home and found a job with a former resident at a Med-Peds private practice. I still yearned for the academic life (yearning = bored out of my skull). After 6 months in private practice, I started looking for an academic position. One of my best friends called and said UM was looking for Med-Peds practitioners. I thought Miami was only a place where my friends' grandparents retired. However, encouraged by the opportunity to resume work in a Med-Peds academic environment, I sent my CV and a few days later, received an email requesting an interview. I had a faculty interview and loved it! The next week they called me back and asked if I would interview for the Med-Peds Program Director position. I interviewed and got the job and here I am. NEVER SAY DIE!

In 2008, I joined UM's Med-Peds program as the only Med-Peds faculty member. I was asked to write a five-year strategic plan for myself and for the program. I asked for what I wanted and followed my own advice, please read rule numbers 3 and 4. My requests were granted and with departmental and categorical program support I was able to recruit faculty and build a successful program. When I first started, I would ask the categorical program directors questions such as, can I change the curriculum to add this subject? After about a month the Pediatric program director said, "It's your program why do you keep asking for permission?" And this is a statement he still regrets.

Lesson #6
Ask for what you want, when you want it. *And don't wait until you are almost dead (2007) to ask for life-saving measures (aka WHAT YOU NEED OR WANT) at work or in your personal life.*

Rule #6
If you don't volunteer, you get "voluntold."

I use a shared decision-making model in leadership and clinical care with residents, and with faculty, division chiefs, and chairs. My style relies on shared responsibility. I am known for coining the phrase, "if you don't volunteer, you get voluntold." My favorite personal tactic is to send emails to faculty that begin with, "Congratulations, due to your overwhelming popularity with the residents, and excellent teaching ability, you have been chosen as (insert committee position here)." When I send emails to one of my many managers, I begin with "I think you would be perfect to do X. What is your availability?"

Unfortunately, what goes around comes around and it came around to me in 2014. We had a new Chair of Medicine and I asked for a meeting to discuss Med-Peds. I arrived at the meeting with my folder full of Med-Peds outcomes data (see rule #2), program information, match data, outcomes data, data, and more data. After I spoke for 10 minutes he said, "I have a proposal for you." I said, "Okay." He said, "I want you to be the Vice Chair of Education for the Department of Medicine." My response was shock and I said, "What?! Why?!" My internal critic responded in my head with, "You are an insane person. What gives you the idea you can do that job?!" By the way, never give a voice to the comments of your internal critic. He said, "Because you were recommended." I said, "By who?!" He would not tell me. I then asked about the performance expectations and the job description. He told me I had two days to think about it and to not reveal the offer to anyone. I left the office and immediately called my mother and the Pediatric program director (my work husband/work issue therapist). Yes, I called back two days later and accepted the job offer. That's when I learned about the voluntold bomb. "By the way, this job comes with the Medicine program director job. You can choose the new Med-Peds program director or we can do a search." Ouch. Okay. Panic. Deep breath. See rules 3 and 4. I asked, "Can I have a day to think about it?" He said yes. I didn't really want to leave the MedPeds program director role. With Med-Peds as my lifelong work, I also realized if you turn down a job from your new boss, it is unlikely you'll be offered another promotion. I also realized in the words of Wayne Gretzky, "You miss 100% of the shots you never take" and I said yes and accepted the offer letter outlining the department's expectations for my new role including things I wanted (see Rule 5). My new role kept me in the Med-Peds clinical area, and I could participate in any Pediatric education activities during my administrative time (as if anyone could stop me), and my Peds clinical time didn't change.

Lesson #7
Live what you have learned and don't forget your rules.
Rule #7
Know your worth in dollars and sense (not a typo)!

Just a few years ago in 2017, I thought once again I was content. I received a speaker invitation to address the Med-Peds conference 50th anniversary celebration about my career. In my estimation at this point my career had progressed as a long slow fall down the stairs. I began on a stair stayed there for a while then fell onto a new stair, it is not as if I walked or ran quickly. Gravity, or being in the "right place, at the right time," put me on a specific stair. At the end of my remarks, I mentioned my new goal of trying to be more self-directed in my career. It was time to pursue jobs I wanted and not wait to be recruited. Annually on New Year's Day I make new life goals and similarly at the start of the academic year I make new work-life goals. In case you are wondering, work-life is a single hyphenated word (at least in my opinion) because if work-life balance exists, then work is not part of life. However, for those of us who are physicians, work is a large part of our lives. We spend more of our awake time working than at home, unless you sleep only a few hours a night. But, I digress.

After that speech, I received an email, and several emails from the chair at another institution asking me to interview for a Division Chief position. He had heard me speak. I politely declined several times and agreed to go for a visit which was really a full interview day. I loved the people, the place, their mission, and the idea of doing something different and new. And most of all, I was excited about being valued for what I had to offer. I was formally offered the job at my second interview. I started mulling it over… and I asked myself "are you right for this job?" and then I remembered lesson #7. I shed the imposter syndrome and reminded myself that I was recruited and asked myself, "do I want this job? Is this the right time and place for ME? If I take this position will my career move forward in a direction that I want to go?" (See rules 3 – 5, Lessons 4 – 6). My short answer was no. My longer answer was it is a great opportunity and while not exactly what I wanted, I loved the people, their mission, and the place. I thought about my current situation at UM. I asked myself am I getting everything I want here? Am I moving in the direction that I want to go? Am I moving forward? The short answer was no. The long answer was I am very content and able to do many things that I want, but I want more and now is the right time to ask for it. I told both department chairs about the offer and I asked for what I wanted. The first answer was "you can't have that, but you can have this." I said, "No thanks." Then there was a request to meet with the Dean. I shared some of my story and he asked what I wanted. I told him and added some new things. In response my retention offer came with a yes, although with some exceptions I accepted. I know how much I'm worth and I asked for the full amount which came with financial responsibility and a new title. And I got it.

The final lesson: Don't let anyone tell you what you are worth. You show them, tell them, and if they don't give it to you, say goodbye. ■

Omaida C. Velazquez, MD

Professor and Chair, DeWitt Daughtry Family Department of Surgery
David Kimmelman Endowed Chair in Vascular Surgery
Surgeon-in-Chief for UMHC/UHealth System &
Jackson Health System
University of Miami Miller School of Medicine

For the last four years I served as the Chair of the DeWitt Daughtry Family Department of Surgery at UM Miller School of Medicine and Surgeon-in-Chief for the UM and Jackson Health System (JHS). Over the past decade I also served for three years as Executive Dean for Research at the Miller School of Medicine and eight years as Chief of the Division of Vascular and Endovascular Surgery in the Department of Surgery at the UM and Jackson Health System. Over the last two decades of my academic career, my goal was always focused on contributing to society through clinical service, teaching, and/or discovery.

I was born and raised in rural Pinar Del Rio, Cuba, during a time when basic modern amenities we often take for granted such as electricity, running water, indoor plumbing, paved floors, and basic freedoms were not accessible. I have very few photographs of my early years but the ones we have convey a remarkably humble life. My family always nurtured our dream for better days. By the age of fourteen I had moved over six times as my parents endlessly pursued a better life and freedom. In May of 1980 at the age of 14, I experienced the most transformational relocation of my life to Union City, New Jersey.

As a child, I often dreamed of traveling to the U.S. although it seemed so improbable. One memorable afternoon after an early release from school I returned home to find my mom and dad hastily packing. I remember the big suitcase and thought during our previous moves we had never packed such a big suitcase. I wondered where did that luggage come from? I wasn't told in advance, but we were about to join the 1980 Mariel Boatlift, invited by our family who had immigrated to the U.S. in the early 1960s. On that day I witnessed the best and worst of human nature. We survived the government-orchestrated departure mobs, followed by a week of detention in open-air concentration camp-like conditions at the port of Mariel. We survived a hellish trip in an overcrowded lobster fishing boat, filled to the brim with exiles, over stormy seas and arrived at Key West, Florida. I vividly remember the Spanish-speaking volunteers that greeted us with Coca-Cola and M&Ms. I was severely dehydrated and dreadfully nauseous, but I remember their kind and caring welcome as if we had arrived in heaven and were received by angels.

Later, as we flew to Fort Chaffee, Arkansas, I was elated by being able to drink water, eat food, and the excitement of my very first airplane ride. But the elation would quickly recede and be replaced by an almost out-of-body experience that swept over me during the entire month we were held there. I couldn't understand the language of the helpful staff. The food was entirely new and a shock to my system although now I'm aware that it was healthy and nutritious. We were held for many days behind barbed wire containment walls. Inevitably, tempers flared, there were riots and dorm fires deliberately started by delinquent, hopeless refugees without families to come and meet them. The family men took shifts guarding the dorms by day and night. My day-to-day existence reminded me of a scene from one of those old sub-titled black-and-white movies I had seen as a child (but without the subtitles). I was unaware of the political forces and debates going on outside of that camp about our immigration. It would take many years for me to fully understand. For many years afterwards, every experience in America felt surreal, from the escalators to the revolving doors to the individually packaged products discovered during trips to the supermarket.

The negative stigma attached to Mariel immigrants, as portrayed by the media, haunted me and threatened to derail my progress. Although I was offered political asylum and became an American citizen, for a long time I felt branded by the negativity associated with the word "marielita." For decades, I never voluntarily spoke about my background. I envisioned a marvelous path of self-realization, contribution, and fulfillment. I knew it would take a great deal of hard work to figure out how to realize my vision.

In retrospect, today, 39 years after I arrived in the U.S., I'm mystified as to how I navigated my circuitous path. Truthfully, a great deal of it came down to my perseverance, adaptability, intuition, willfulness, and great mentorship and some very good luck. My ambitious goals were simply to become a doctor, help people, discover new cures. Although as a reserved and understated young woman who arrived in the U.S. in 1980 not able to speak a word of English, how would I achieve success? I was an immigrant, a Latina woman, committed from the beginning to traverse the unknown terrain of medical academia. I was determined and fearless. Failure was not an option. My first step, after arriving in the U.S. only three years before was getting into college. Among my large extended family in the U.S., I was the first to attend college, so none of my family had been down this path before. Yet, from a young and tender age my father stressed that education and hard work were important. Even in first grade, if I came home with a test score of 99, my father would ask if anyone else in the class scored 100 and if so, he asked why didn't I? From the beginning of my school days I embraced the pursuit of excellence. In Union City, New Jersey, I attended an inner city public high school where I graduated as one of the top five seniors in my class. One of my teachers, Nadia Makar, took me under her wing and became a life-long advisor and sponsor.

I went on to attain my Bachelor of Science degree with high honors and thesis from the Stevens Institute of Technology. Four years later, in 1991, I graduated as the class Valedictorian from the University of Medicine and Dentistry of New Jersey (UMDNJ), New Jersey Medical School. After going to college and medical school with my life-long closest friend Dr. Romulo Cuy (Rom), we married. Our lives had been entwined on the path to becoming medical doctors. I trained in General Surgery and Vascular Surgery at the University of Pennsylvania (UPenn). Our son, Peter James Cuy (Jimmy) was born during my two years of formal research training, which were routinely added to the standard 5-year clinical surgery training. After vascular fellowship, I joined the Faculty of the University of Pennsylvania, Board Certified in General and Vascular Surgery and served eight years and became a tenured Associate Professor. During my seventh year on faculty at UPenn, our daughter, Julia Caridad Cuy, was born. My department chairs at UPenn, Dr. Barker and later Dr. Kaiser, were highly supportive of my career. I was greatly honored when UPenn Dean Dr. Arthur Rubenstein asked me to consider staying at UPenn. With many friends and great opportunities I had a wonderful professional family at UPenn. It wasn't an easy decision to move, but the desire to spread my wings to take on a major leadership role and to live closer to my parents were all important factors in my decision.

The road to success was bumpy, but there were many kind and selfless good Samaritans along the way. I never fully grasped their significance as I attained one professional milestone then another. With their guidance I successfully built a strong track record of academic productivity and achievement. As I built more than a decade of professional experience, I wanted to offer my contributions to a community that would be miles away from the institutions and my safety net of mentors. Fortunately, I was presented with a range of opportunities but didn't feel secure to take the next step. It took years (and trusted advice from great surgeons), and that next step guided me to a complex of affiliated hospitals under private, county, and federal fiscal management – UM, Jackson Health System (JHS), and Miami VA Health System. My timing was not ideal, as the US economy was on the brink of a great recession and the fiscal pressures in many academic health systems were well known. Two months after I began work, UM purchased its first acute care hospital and overnight my initial responsibilities duplicated. Luckily the new hospital was on the same campus and within walking distance. The proximity of the institutions strained the pre-existing long-term relationships built over decades with other adjacent health systems. Program building was sorely needed in the modern vascular and endovascular disciplines and in surgical research. Much like a boat at sea, the weather was not always fair. But I've always been energized by great challenges.

In September of 2007, I was offered an opportunity of a lifetime as the Vascular Division Chief and Associate Professor of Surgery at the University of Miami (UM) and Jackson Memorial Hospital. After living and working in the northeast US for 27 years and contributing to the University of Pennsylvania for sixteen years I joined UM. With my husband, Rom, and our children, 12-year-old Jimmy, and 6-month-old Julia we moved to beautiful Miami. As the new Division Chief of Vascular my mission was to develop a modern vascular and endovascular service encompassing all the academic disciplines (clinical, research, education, and community service).

My work began under the truly inspirational leadership of UM President, Dr. Donna E. Shalala, and Miller School of Medicine and UM Health System CEO, Dr. and Medical School Dean Pascal Goldschmidt, and the support of my Chair, Dr. Alan Livingstone. Livingstone had been extremely charming and persistent and personally recruited me during visits to Philadelphia several times over the preceding three years. He expressed strong trust and support of my research and experience. I enjoyed generous autonomy and freely interacted with leadership from all the hospitals. As the only female division Chief, my colleagues and the other division Chiefs and our Department Chair were all gracious and welcoming. Soon after I embraced Miami and its warmth and diversity as my beloved third home. I found my new home to be a great professional and academic fit that also extended to my personal life. I treasured being close to my parents and giving them the opportunity to bond with their grandchildren. Miami seemed like the ideal residence for Rom and me to serve, contribute, and continue to grow in both of our personal and professional lives.

Soon after I joined UM, in 2007, I was instrumental in finalizing commitments for a transformational endowment designated for vascular research. After some discussions with the executor of the gift, the endowment founded the David Kimmelman Endowed Chair that I now hold, in addition to committing to the $500,000 annual funding dedicated to limb salvage vascular research. Every year, I meet with the executor of the endowment to report on our progress and to secure the continuity of the foundation's commitment and success for vascular research. Their gift was extended twice and verbally extended in perpetuity for as long as the Foundation continues to financially thrive. The vascular division also secured multiple additional private philanthropic donations, other foundation gifts, and industry funding for academic programmatic support.

Clinically, my work focused on endovascular and open-surgical treatment of vascular diseases. In 2010, I was promoted to professor with tenure at the UM School of Medicine. In my role leading the Vascular & Endovascular Division, I recruited a strong, diverse, and complementary team that has tremendously advanced the clinical, research, and educational missions at UM. The Vascular and Endovascular Division grew from three to nine academic clinical faculty members and four dedicated vascular research faculty members. We successfully expanded clinical services to all five of the health district's major hospitals (University of Miami Hospital and Clinics (UMHC), Jackson Memorial Hospital (JMH), The Miami Veterans Administration Hospital (Miami VAH), and satellites – Jackson North and Jackson South Hospital. As a result of the quick clinical expansion including a steep growth curve in case volumes and complexity for vascular cases, we established the essential foundation for the start of a new Vascular Fellowship training program, formally accredited in 2011.

Despite the global economic downturn of 2008-2010 with associated leadership transitions, we successfully secured funding and drafted the training curriculum for the first ACGME/RRC accredited vascular surgery training program in the South Florida region and in the history of the UM and JHS. These education efforts were led by my first faculty recruit to Miami, a great friend and colleague, the late Dr. JJ Karmacharya. The untimely death of Dr. Karmacharya in a tragic plane accident shook the very foundation of our young vascular team, but we were resilient and continued to build, always remembering to honor his many contributions. Currently, in addition to the Vascular independent Fellowship, a Vascular Residency training program was founded and ACGME/RRC accredited in 2016. Both training programs remain highly competitive, continuously accredited, and in good standing, with a 100% board passage rate to-date.

Concurrent to clinical expansion and establishing training programs, the research infrastructure and scientific talent pool was rapidly expanded to include over 15 members (MDs, PhDs, students, staff and research coordinators) mentored and overseen initially by me and subsequently by the faculty members that I recruited, mentored, and appointed. Work from my research laboratory team resulted in seminal contributions in the area of angiogenesis, vasculogenesis, and wound healing. These scientific contributions are relevant to unsolved diseases in the field of Vascular and Endovascular Surgery such as peripheral vascular disease (PAD), critical limb ischemia (CLI), and non-healing diabetic chronic wounds. For these contributions, I was inducted into the American Society for Clinical Investigation (ASCI), an honor not frequently bestowed on a surgeon-scientist.

Serving as the site principal investigator (PI), I have also brought several multi-center industry-sponsored trials and National Institutes of Health (NIH)-sponsored clinical studies to UM in the areas of aortic aneurysms, aortic trauma, carotid disease, and peripheral arterial disease. As a surgeon-scientist, I've served as PI for several major NIH grant awards as a continuously-funded NIH researcher for over 15 years. In April 2014

I served as the PI for an R01, research to investigate the contributing role of Notch signaling and bone marrow-derived stem cell traffic in the pathogenesis and progression of atherosclerosis. Recently in May 2019, I became the PI on another R01, to evaluate E-Selectin gene and cell-based therapies in wound healing and critical limb ischemia (CLI). Efforts from my laboratory led to a new gene and cell-based therapy that may one day eradicate the need for many types of amputations. This novel approach was patented by UM and is currently under an exclusive license option between UM and a venture capital group that intends to fund the remaining pre-clinical and clinical testing requisite to FDA-approval for clinical application.

Starting in 2011, I was appointed to serve as the Vice Chair for Research in the Department of Surgery, a service that soon evolved into a subsequent appointment, from 2012 to 2015, as the Executive Dean for Research (EDR), Research Education, and Innovative Medicine for the UM Miller School of Medicine. My role was to restructure and optimize the administrative support for the medical school's research. Working with the medical school Dean, Dr. Goldschmidt, I served as a thought leader for the medical school's scientific portfolio and research priorities. Throughout those years, despite many institutional financial challenges, the UM Miller School of Medicine's research portfolio and national rankings strengthened and the school secured funding for the first cycle of a NIH CTSA (Clinical Translation Science Award). Growth in the research mission was achieved, despite the previous reduction in the support work force in research administration. This was a greatly rewarding role that offered the opportunity to interact, support, and collaborate with many of UM's brilliant investigators.

In 2015, the UM/Jackson Chair of Surgery who had recruited me eight years before, Dr. Alan Livingstone, stepped down, after 17 years of illustrious leadership. UM conducted a 9-month long national search for his successor. As a result, I was appointed Chair of Surgery and Inaugural Surgeon-in-Chief for both Health Systems (UM and Jackson). During my tenure as Chair, we have experienced growth in the departmental endowment, expanded our faculty, and increased our research efforts. Additionally, the clinical mission was strengthened as indicated by sustained year-over-year significant increases in new patient visits, established patient visits, and volume of surgeries. Concurrently, substantial improvements in clinical key performance indicators (length of stay, 30-day perioperative mortality, and 30-day readmission rates) were achieved. Diversity was an intentional priority in talent acquisition. Among the new faculty hires, more than 50% were women and/or from underrepresented minority groups. Collaboration with other departments, centers, and institutes was instrumental to many strategic recruitments aimed at expanding clinical services and increasing academic impact among the top institutional priorities (i.e. cancer, trauma, cardiovascular, and transplantation).

My journey so far has been unpredictable and rewarding. It would have not been possible without many role models, mentors, and sponsors that guided me and helped me along the way (the many good Samaritans in my life). Let me share that life always presents abundant challenges and harsh critics. As the first Latina to chair an academic department of surgery in the U.S., I would have been naïve to expect any type of "easy pass." I often relied on a guiding principle throughout my personal and professional journey that came from my father: "Time will pass." Time will pass whether one is being productive, accomplishing, changing the world or whether one just idles in unproductive self-indulgence. Time will pass and what seems unbearable now will be just fine tomorrow. What elates you today should be cherished, never taken for granted, because time will pass, and the sunny days will give way to threatening thunderstorms.

It is a simple concept that keeps me steady, never too low or too high, never bewildered no matter how hard the task or situation at hand may be, never overreacting to either well-deserved or unmerited criticism. During surgical residency training, one of my research mentors, Dr. John Rombeau, at the University of Pennsylvania reinforced the concept as it applies to perseverance in research.

Another mantra emerged over the years as I've observed (and sometimes personally experienced) the fickle and biased ways of our world. Although I consider myself a person of faith, I've never been devout or religious. Yet, my second mantra emerged from a segment of the Lord's Prayer (a time-honored Christian prayer that I had memorized from childhood). It is a segment that I always recited in a perfunctory way, without much thought about it's deeper meaning: "…and forgive our trespasses as we forgive those who trespass against us…" which is too long for my surgical mind, so I have further shortened it to simply "as we forgive those who trespass against us."

Previously I always focused on the first part of that statement ("forgive our trespasses"), because the list of things I wished I'd done differently is long enough. However, over time I realized the most important part of that statement and the only thing that we can control, is the second part; how "we forgive those who trespass against us." In this prayer, one cannot achieve the first part without the second. I had not previously thought of the meaning in that way. Since this revelation, when I observe behaviors clearly motivated by either implicit bias or conscious and malicious self-serving reasons, I internally refrain "as we forgive those who trespass against us." It reminds me that we all suffer from implicit bias and somehow it alleviates the consternation and chronic irritation, so I choose to free my psychological energy for much more constructive thoughts.

Whether justified or not, women leaders often get more of their fair share of harsh criticism. That may be one of the many reasons why there is such a salient underrepresentation of women in positions of leadership in academic surgery and in the field of medicine in general. Unfortunately, too often, unquestioned implicit bias toward women leaders becomes destructive false narratives: For example, "A set-back is an obvious sign of overall weakness, a great success is the result of a male colleague's talent or intervention, and a well-earned leadership opportunity is the result of someone's charitable attempt to ensure diversity."

Too often a woman's hard work, smarts, demonstration of skill, and track record of excellence and success are unrecognized or underappreciated or attributed to someone else. If I said I've never experienced these things along the way, it would be disingenuous. But "time will pass" and society will face and choose to deal with the terrible side effects of implicit bias and hopefully, choose to not tolerate that behavior any longer. Along the way, when I occasionally encounter obvious prejudice, it gives me an opportunity to forgive as we all wish for our own trespasses to be forgiven. Nevertheless, it is every leader's duty (myself included) not to be complacent with the status quo related to well-recognized lingering and pervasive gender biases in the workplace. I'm proud and fortunate to be part of an institution with a tradition of fairness and inclusiveness, forged by prior leadership (such as President Shalala and CEO/Dean Goldschmidt), and prioritized and perpetuated by current leadership, President Frenk, CEO Abraham, and Dean Ford. ■

Ana E. Campo, MD

Professor of Clinical Psychiatry
Associate Dean for Student Affairs
Director For Medical Student Education in Psychiatry
University of Miami Miller School of Medicine

I'm going to share the story of how I left my homeland and how the past shaped who I am today. My story includes the forces that contributed to my becoming a child psychiatrist and teacher living in a land of freedom and opportunity.

In the middle of Central America, El Salvador, comprised of approximately 8,124 square miles, is a beautiful tiny country, smaller than Massachusetts. El Salvador is also full of beautiful flowers, dense vegetation, volcanoes, and blue skies. On the Pacific Ocean are black volcanic sand beaches with huge waves. I fondly recall my country also widely known as the "little midget of America." My childhood memories were of a peaceful land, going to the beach, lying on hammocks, seeing millions of stars at night, and going to sleep and waking up to the sound of the ocean.

My parents were very wise and enrolled me at an American School so I could learn English. From kindergarten to high school, I had an "American education" with U.S. civics, U.S. history, and all things American. When my father, a civil engineer, got accepted to a one-year postgraduate course at Purdue University in West Lafayette, Indiana, my mother, brother and I went with him. It was easy for me to adapt to 5th grade in the U.S. because I could already speak English. But to my surprise, no one in Indiana knew where El Salvador was geographically located. Some people thought it was the place Christopher Columbus first landed in America. But regardless, I was happy. While living in Indiana, for the first time I went to a K-mart, saw squirrels, snow and apple trees. When I returned to the American school in El Salvador for 6th grade, I was not saying "yes" but "yeah." My teachers reprimanded me for using American slang, but I felt cool. I always knew I wanted to return and experience more of North America.

Several years later as I progressed through high school like most of my American School classmates, I wanted to come to the U.S. to go to college. However, since my plan was to attend medical school, my parents learned at that time, U.S.-based medical schools wouldn't accept international students. So, if I graduated from college in the U.S., I would have to go back to El Salvador for medical school. Therefore, I stayed in El Salvador and much to my dismay, my dreams of coming to the U.S. evaporated for a short time.

I began college at the National University of El Salvador together with thousands of other 18-year-old students who had dreams of going to medical school. There, as in many European countries, you enter the university after high school, complete two years of undergraduate school and then enter medical school. After four years of medical school, you complete a year of internship and a year of "social service" to reimburse the government for a free education. This allows the government to provide public health care to the lower socioeconomic classes in countryside public health clinics. By year two, most of the students were weeded out and only about 300 students were ready to start anatomy and medical school courses. During my first year, my father died of a heart attack at the young age of forty-four. My mother taught at the American School and my brothers were nine and six-years-old when our father died. His death was one of the most terrible losses our family suffered, but my mother is a very strong woman, very brave and hardworking and ultimately, we all fared well.

During medical school, I enjoyed studying, made a lot of friends, and was content. But in the mid- to late-seventies civil strife began affecting the country. There were extreme political groups of every perspective, the extreme right, the death squads, the extreme left, the guerrillas, and many other splinter groups belonging to both sides. El Salvador became a country of extreme geopolitical interest to the superpowers. For the the next decade, the Salvadorean government, supported by the Carter and Reagan administrations, engaged in a civil war with guerillas who also had their own sources of funding and support from other leftist countries including Nicaragua, Cuba, and Russia. The fighting in the countryside and poor neighborhoods around the capital and big cities increased, though our medical school education continued without interruption. In the late 1970's, the government became suspicious of the National University students, as it promoted propaganda that both the law students and the medical students were "subversive" and leaning to the "left." With our American school education, me and some of my university classmates were branded as aligning with "imperialist" forces. I had to learn to navigate those conflicts and the potential pitfalls. One of my strategies was to become an academic tutor for my classmates and as such, became needed and not ostracized for belonging to the "bourgeoisie" with its conventional attitudes. I didn't know yet that academia and teaching would be in my future.

During these years, several times the government closed the university for weeks and months with our classes interrupted but eventually we would return. As urban demonstrations and government protests became more frequent, I was already doing rotations in hospitals, the equivalent of clerkships in U.S. medical schools. As a result of street demonstrations and protests the wounded victims of military shootings came to the hospitals where I was doing my rotations. I still remember the images including those of some of our classmates, who had gone to protest, been caught in the crossfire, and were wounded and killed.

One day in late 1979, we were alerted that students and young people were called to take up arms and join the guerilla groups in the mountains. We all heard this through the grapevine at the main campus of the National University. Many of my friends joined the military effort and some never returned home. El Salvador became a chaotic place before I left. In March 1980, Monsignor Romero was gunned down at the National Cathedral. The left said it was the right, the right said it was the left. In July 1980, the National University was ransacked by government troops and closed. This time it would remain closed for the next four years.

Since the University was closed at that time and there was no other medical school in the country, several of my classmates and I started trying to go abroad to continue our clinical rotations, but most of the other medical schools in Central America and Mexico wouldn't accept and credit us for our recent work. I started studying for my ECFMG and passed it – one of the happiest days of my life! I knew it was a ticket to eventually return to the States. In 1981, the father of one of my medical school friends who worked for an international agency and transferred to the Dominican Republic (DR), learned the DR would accept our credits. Since we were in the same situation, we found a DR-based private medical school to accept our credits. My friend's family graciously allowed me to live with them for one year while we finished school. The toughest part of leaving El Salvador was leaving my mom and two brothers who were still in high school, but I had to go. Within the next three years, both of my brothers left El Salvador to study medicine in Costa Rica and eventually came to the States for residency, too. After I left, civil war continued for the next ten years until 1992, when peace accords were finally signed in Mexico between the different groups. Eventually it would be reported that over 75,000 people died in the civil war and still many more disappeared.

That one year in the Dominican Republic was a respite from all the chaos I was surrounded by in El Salvador. A few months before graduation in March 1982, I decided since I had not registered for the National Resident Matching Program, I flew to Miami to see if I could "scramble" into a residency position. As luck would have it, that year was 1982 and the previous year *Time* magazine had just published a cover story declaring South Florida as "Paradise Lost" given its crime and decline. US medical students did not want to train in Miami. But to me, no amount of crime would even begin to compare to what I left behind. I was able to "scramble" and secure a psychiatry residency position at Jackson Memorial Hospital as during that year, only two of the six open psychiatry residency positions were filled through the Match.

Jackson Memorial Hospital always felt like a haven. I was grateful for everything I had, and mainly for my education and training. Work didn't seem like work. Helping patients with despair, anxiety, and psychosis was for many years what I had yearned to do. I was "living the dream." During my training, I had wonderful teachers and attending physicians who taught me so much. Once I graduated from residency, teaching was always important to me and academic medicine was more appealing than going into private practice. In 1987, after I finished my fellowship in child and adolescent psychiatry, I decided to stay on the faculty in the UM Miller School of Medicine Department of Psychiatry. I became actively involved in organized psychiatry, and again found many mentors who encouraged me along the way to seek leadership positions and pursue scholarly work.

My children were born and raised and in South Florida. For us, as for many immigrants, South Florida was never "Paradise Lost" but "Paradise Found." I feel tremendous respect towards all my American school classmates who were brave, stayed in El Salvador, and weathered the war. I feel sadness for all of my university classmates and other family and friends who lost their lives and after the war were not heard from again. My bi-cultural upbringing in both Salvadorean and American schools contributed to my ability to accept dichotomous situations and navigate conflict. I feel grateful as hard as those times were prior to leaving; the adversity helped me to become resilient. I believe my desire to understand the complexities of human motivation and behavior put me on a path to become a psychiatrist. My ability to help children living with psychic distress and agony was also fulfilling.

My work teaching medical students has always been inspiring and provided my greatest motivation. The importance of teaching medical students about both normal and abnormal child and adult development as well as psychiatric disorders is my driving force and still appeals to me as a professor in academic medicine. I believe when you love what you do it becomes evident in your work product and as people around you recognize it, you are rewarded with further opportunities to attain leadership positions. Over fifteen years ago, I still remember when I was asked by the senior associate dean of medical students, to be the ombudsman for the medical students. And I said, yes, without asking if the position included financial compensation. At the time my only thought was it would be fun to help medical students in need. That experience led to other opportunities. In 2005, I became the assistant dean for student services and three years later I transitioned to student affairs. I hope over my last two decades of teaching I have inspired some medical students to pursue careers in psychiatry. I also hope that all the other hundreds of UMMSM graduates who have elected to do residencies other than psychiatry, learned of its importance in the medical field and will always treat psychiatric patients with the respect and dignity they deserve. ■

Elizabeth A. Crocco, MD

Medical Director
UM Memory Disorder Clinic
Center for Cognitive Neuroscience & Aging
Chief, Division of Geriatric Psychiatry
Associate Clinical Professor
Department of Psychiatry and Behavioral Sciences
University of Miami Miller School of Medicine
Geriatric Psychiatry Training Director
Jackson Memorial Hospital

When people ask me when I first knew I wanted to be a doctor, my standard answer is 3 years old. The truth is, I cannot remember a time when I imagined myself being anything else. It's part of the confession I make to both colleagues and friends. I've had only two stable jobs in my entire life: camp counselor and physician. How does one choose their profession at such an early age? Growing up in a working-class neighborhood of Brooklyn, New York, I was the middle child of five in a multigenerational Irish-Italian Catholic family. My father was an academic pulmonary and critical care physician and my mother was a registered nurse. They often shared their titillating and outrageous medical stories with the family. Most famously my parents shared the story of how they met. My father was a medical intern and mother was a nursing student at St. Vincent's Hospital in Greenwich Village. They met standing over the body of a patient named "Chester" as they closed his eyes and pronounced him dead. Like most parents they were complex people. They were obsessive, loud, intrusive, and dramatic, not unlike Woody Allen's parents in his New York City-based films. They were also loving, demonstrative, empathic, and non-judgmental when caring for those in need. For better or worse, they served as my professional role models. I was lucky to be guided and supported by both parents on my long road to achieving my goal!

As I grew up, there were more experiences that guided me to a career in medicine. I was a physically fragile child and was sick more frequently than average children, so I had more contact with medical treatment. I observed physicians armed with their experiences trying to figure out how to alleviate my symptoms. I saw that diagnosing patients was like solving a complex puzzle by devising a solution. And I loved puzzles! I also recognized that having the ability to relate to and understand suffering was just as important as having medical knowledge and skills to solve a puzzle. As I matured, I began to recognize those qualities in myself. My recognition of these strengths reinforced my drive to become a doctor. I felt that I had the temperament, empathy, listening skills, and understanding of human behaviors and motivations to become a good doctor.

My father repeatedly instructed my brothers, sisters, and me to choose careers with a good salary and said the best way to succeed was to pursue higher education. He promoted attaining a college degree and pursuing graduate studies, much later we realized his advice was ahead of its time. It wasn't until I went to high school when I encountered girls whose fathers did not promote independence and self-reliance to their daughters but did so to their sons. Many of the girls I met had fathers who did not prioritize education as the most important step to adulthood. Instead their fathers suggested marrying and relying on a good husband for support was the way to go. This struck me as a very odd concept, even at that time!

My eldest brother, despite my father's opinion on education, loved to egg me on. "Girls don't become doctors, they can only become nurses," he mockingly used to say. He would tell me I did not have the ability or the stamina. My father laughed at this, but I was angry. My older brother was competitive and half joking to get a rise out of me, as brothers do, and in retrospect, he may have been a bit intimidated by my drive. Recently when I asked my parents how they saw me growing up, my mother put it best. "You were single-minded and unwavering in your pursuit since a young age and there was nothing that could dissuade you from your ultimate goal."

As a teenager, I discovered my mother's old nursing school textbook on psychiatry and after reading it, I was hooked. At 14 years old, I decided to become a psychiatrist. I took psychology classes in high school. I loved the complexity and challenge of human behavior and the brain. What a puzzle to figure out! I told myself I would be objective and would keep an open mind about the other medical specialties. Of course, at that age my concept of psychiatry was not fully formed. I imagined I would become a psychoanalyst and treat patients all day in my Upper East Side Manhattan office as they lay on a couch. I must have had a disturbing psychoanalytical persona as I distinctly remember my boyfriend in high school (who is now my husband) countering any argument we had with, "Why don't you go read your 'Psychology Today'!" I guess my attitude was not always appreciated.

During the 1980's when I was in college, my father spoke to me objectively and dispassionately about medicine. From his own perspective, he would balance the positives with the negatives and I clearly remember all the negatives! He discussed the hard work, years of training, long hours, and delayed gratification. He told me when he was a medical resident, they called you a resident because you literally resided at the hospital, you received room and board for free and they paid you the equivalent of 10 cents an hour. You were always working and referred to the time as if he was an indentured servant. HMOs had arrived at this time. He discussed their effects on private practitioners and how unhappy many physicians were in their profession. Being forced to see too many patients, encountering roadblocks to good clinical decision making, observing the effects of capitation, and middle management making the decisions on which services were reimbursable and which were not, all added to profound dissatisfaction among physicians. He made it clear that he did not want to influence my decision in a positive or negative way, however he did want to set my expectations for a career in modern medicine. His overall advice completely contradicted the joy he expressed when he taught his residents and fellows at Saint Vincent's where he was the Chief of Pulmonary Medicine and Associate Director of Medicine. He regaled me with stories of treating patients with complex diagnoses and clinical research he performed with mentors and mentees. He soberly reported about the bizarre cases of Kaposi's Sarcomas he saw in gay men in the clinics he ran in New York's Greenwich Village. His love and dedication to his work was obvious as he tried to objectively share his experience.

Throughout college I threw myself into the sciences, as well as basic science research in the lab, and did some volunteer clinical work and research with my father and other physicians. I discovered a real love of science and biology. I met other female students that were interested in pursuing MD's and PhD's. I was able to achieve excellent grades and good MCAT scores, but my Pre-Med academic advisors at Rutgers University did not encourage me. They told me I did not have the scores needed for medical school. I was devastated and very reluctant to apply. When I shared that advice with my older female microbiology professor at Douglas College, she replied "You had the highest scores in my microbiology class, given the skills you have demonstrated, if you don't apply, who should?" But the person who truly convinced me was my father's fellow in pulmonary and critical care medicine. He was always a quiet man, and I was surprised when my father told me he wanted to take me to lunch to discuss my future and would not take no for an answer. He took me to a New Jersey diner and asked me straight away why I was reluctant to apply to medical school. I told him about the negative comments from my pre-med advisors. In contrast to their advice, he suggested since he completed the entire physician training process, he was a much better expert than the advisors. He said they were completely full of it and not to listen to them and added he had no doubt that I would be accepted. He was right.

Not all my interactions with physicians were positive ones. One of my father's other fellows started a conversation with me at a holiday party. She told me I should think very hard about going to medical school because she completely regretted becoming a doctor. She described the brutal hours and the negative effects on her personal relationships and any hope for a family. I felt a great deal of empathy for her because she was clearly in pain. I also wisely understood she was describing the burden I may face if I became a physician. Interestingly, I also recognized that she was at a low point in her life. Like a good future psychiatrist, I was gaining insight into understanding human motivation and interactions. Psychologically, she believed she needed to share the reasons why medicine may not have been the right career for her and for me.

I applied to multiple medical schools in the northeast and true to the prediction of my father's former fellow, I had a 50% acceptance rate. I attended Robert Wood Johnson Medical School in New Jersey. It was very difficult compared to college. It felt like an entire semester course load was compressed into one week! Although my medical school class was half female, the school had a very hierarchical structure and I did not feel supported. Daily I was with the same students in the classroom and sometimes it reminded me of high school. Both the men and the women were a highly competitive group, and it was hard to trust anyone. I found the experience very unpleasant. Although all these students were top-tier at their respective colleges not everyone could be top-tier in medical school. I did well and learned a great deal but felt disappointed as it was hard to make any real friends in this highly stressful environment. When I finally entered my 3rd year clerkships, I felt more at home. Honestly, I did not love all the clerkships, but true to my prediction, I remained objective. At the end I couldn't change the fact that the psychiatry clerkship was the one I loved the most.

I completed my residency in psychiatry at Mount Sinai Medical Center in New York. I truly loved it. I met physicians and residents from all over the US and the world. This diversity of both the medical staff and patients was a valuable part of my education as was the medical knowledge. During my first week I met a psychiatrist in my PGY 1 class from the Soviet Union who was completing his residency in the U.S. He said to me, "If you teach me American medical shorthand and abbreviations, I will teach you psychiatry." Throughout our residency we had a mutually beneficial relationship and friendship. I was proud to serve as administrative Chief Resident which was not easy but taught me many leadership skills that I still use daily. However, my experience with psychodynamic psychiatry and psychoanalytic training, however, did not go as well. I still adored the theory but in our first class, a supervisor instructed us that in order to be successful at psychodynamic psychotherapy, we must stay in a sort of "box" where you become a "blank slate" for your patients to project their own transference onto you. There were many rules. You cannot touch, hug, share with your patients or have pictures in your office, to name just a few. This was a major problem as it didn't fit well with my background and family's style of demonstrative love and embraces. I also learned over time that patients must spend many years in this type of therapy. My patients were in pain and I needed to alleviate their suffering as fast as possible! I began to drift towards more evidence-based behavioral and biologically-based treatment to quickly and effectively treat their suffering.

One day during my PGY-3 year in New York with three feet of snow on the ground, my husband at the time, convinced me to move to Florida for a better lifestyle after residency. I was reluctant to go because, like most New Yorkers, I believed that NYC was the center of the universe. I also knew I always wanted to be an academic psychiatrist in New York. After doing some research, the only place that fit my work criteria in Florida was the University of Miami/Jackson Memorial Hospital. I surmised Miami was an attractive big diverse city, but I knew almost nothing about the psychiatry department. When the Chair of Psychiatry at Mount Sinai Medical Center in New York discovered my plans he completely flipped out. "You want to do what!?! Go where!?!" he shouted. He told me the move would ruin my career. Clearly, I did not listen. I anxiously applied to the fellowship in Geriatric Psychiatry. Remember, before I wanted to be a psychoanalyst, now I was going to treat agitated, cognitively impaired patients with dementia? I gave it a chance and discovered the specialty fit me perfectly! In 1998, after my one-year fellowship serving as Chief Fellow in geriatric psychiatry, UM offered me the Assistant Clinical Professor of Psychiatry position. I was 30-years-old.

As a young attending, I was thrilled to work with my new patients. I met wonderful faculty and mentors that helped guide my career and with whom I've remained close friends for over 20 years. I also met faculty and supervisors that did not have my best interests at heart. After I had spent two years as a faculty member of the department, one of my colleagues called me into his office and asked, "Why are you doing all that work reviewing medical charts and providing administrative work on the psychiatry unit?" I told him because my immediate supervisor asked me to do so. His reply was, "You do know that he gets paid about $100,000 annually as Medical Director and that is part of his job? Since I had not been paid extra for my hard work, I quietly stopped doing the assigned work. It never came up again.

Work became more difficult after my two boys were born. When they were very young, I took care of them. I learned to work fast and multitask. I didn't have enough time to conduct a lot of clinical research and I could rarely travel to conferences. I did a great deal of clinical work and learned the most from the greatest teachers I could ever have – my patients and their families. I loved teaching my trainees. I had no difficulty catching up later when my children became older and entered high school and college.

As one colleague used to advise me, "Academic achievement and promotion is not a race." I went at my own speed. Currently, my husband and I have been married for 15 years. He was my childhood sweetheart. We decided early on he would be a stay-at-home father, and this worked very well for us. I was very lucky he loved taking central role in our family and fully supported me in my career.

I am now an Associate Clinical Professor of Psychiatry and Behavioral Sciences at UM Miller School of Medicine. I am the Chief of Geriatric Psychiatry, Director of the Geriatric Psychiatry Training Program, and Medical Director of the Center for Cognitive Neuroscience and Aging (CNSA). I work with several young men and women and I'm their teacher and mentor. The group includes medical students, research assistants, residents, fellows, and young faculty. I try to be a role model by sharing how women with a family can achieve academic excellence in medicine and love their work.

The more leadership roles you accept the more experience you gain, and the work becomes more challenging. I will not lie to you. When I was young faculty I was regarded as kind and giving. Most at work still see me as nice and helpful, but I have heard over the years several female physicians myself included called names for being outspoken. Be prepared and realize there may be leadership meetings during which your comments are cut off and not widely shared. Many women do the work that is difficult and time consuming yet receive no promotions or accolades. In one leadership meeting, a senior faculty member publicly told me that I had a "nervous condition" when I vehemently tried to get my point across and disagreed with him!

I offer this sage advice to all young female physician scientists. Please remember "to thine own self be true." Don't ever try to emulate someone you are not. Embrace who you are and what you love. Keep an open mind and explore different aspects of medicine you previously have not appreciated. Mentors help enormously, and may appear as men, women, young or old. They may not even work in your profession or industry. Their most important quality is that they want to be invested in YOU. Before presenting your data, make sure you have thoroughly done your research. Know how to negotiate and don't forget you are worth the salary and the job you're asking for! When your children are young, you often can't do it all. But they are only young once and your career is long! When you go on maternity leave it's the same old story, all the non-mothers freak out and act like they can't work without you, and all the mothers comment you will be back before you know it! It goes so fast! No one is irreplaceable at work, but you are irreplaceable at home. ■

Mary Bartlett Bunge, PhD

Former Christine E. Lynn Distinguished Professor of Neuroscience
Professor Emerita of Cell Biology, Neurological Surgery, and Neurology
Doctor of Humane Science, honoris causa
University of Miami Miller School of Medicine

From Bench to Bedside: From Investigation of the Biology of Schwann Cells to their Transplantation into Human Spinal Cord Injuries

Essex, a beautiful small and historic town situated at the mouth of the Connecticut River, was an ideal place to grow up. It was a town that could be explored fully by bicycle without the threat of danger in the late thirties and forties. Our home was perched on a hill, leading to its name of "Singing Hills," with woodlands at its back and a sloping grade leading to a picturesque stream in front. The woods and stream provided many hours of investigation and enjoyment for an only child. Lazy afternoons in the warmer months were often spent in my rowboat watching the living organisms in the water. The tiny frogs and tadpoles especially sparked my interest in biology. I realized only later how important all these activities were in fostering my independent nature.

Early years were also filled with many other activities befitting an only child: care of collections of various things (including stamps), creating artistic scrapbooks, reading, drawing and painting, writing, photography, and engaging in arts and crafts. I was very active in Girl Scouts. My parents sought my opinion in family decisions. My very talented maternal grandmother taught me to sew, crochet, appliqué, and knit. After outgrowing sewing clothes for my dolls and nearing high school, I started to design and sew my own clothes. Some even accompanied me to college.

During these childhood years, I admired four heroines. One was Sonja Henie, an Olympic award-winning skater who brought grace and beauty to figure skating. Another was Anna Pavlova, one of the most famous ballerinas of all time. She was famous for her Swan dance. I loved my ballet lessons that inspired serious modern dance performances in college. A third was Marie Curie after finding books about her in our small-town library. I still do not understand why I thought stirring pitchblende month after month was so inspiring. She won not one but two Nobel prizes. Lastly, I was proud to escort Eleanor Roosevelt to the stage for a lecture at a local high school after having been chosen by the Girl Scouts to do so. Artists and a scientist were admired alike.

A disadvantage of the small town was the disappointing education. But my teacher in the 4th grade introduced me to living one-celled organisms; I thought paramecia were beautiful and loved drawing them. I loved the combination of art and science, a continuing priority throughout my life. I was raised by very artistic parents. My mother was a painter and home decorator and my father, an excellent violinist and music teacher who turned later to building beautiful homes and renovating very old houses. (One of the Essex homes we lived in had been built by Captain Ebenezer Williams in 1787.) But in many classes at school I had to dodge erasers and chalk. Also, I was different because I loved learning. It was thus a relief when I entered Northfield School for Girls as a high school junior. This was a turning point.

Enrollment at Simmons College in Boston followed. I chose this college because its founder envisioned a combined liberal arts and practical education for women. The college offered a major in biology with a focus on medical technology, my occupational goal. But this goal was to change. In the summer following my junior year, I was accepted into the college student summer program at Jackson Laboratories in Bar Harbor, Maine. This afforded me exposure to high quality lectures and laboratory research as well as to a community of highly motivated students destined for graduate or medical school. The faculty invited us to their homes; in one case I helped lay out a new patio. It was the best summer of my life! A fragment of rabbit heart that continued to beat in tissue culture stirred my interest in research and new thoughts of applying to graduate school. My mentor, Dr. Philip White, an unusual Jackson faculty member because he studied tree tumors instead of animal tissue, asked me soon after my arrival to change the medium in his 22 year old tomato root cultures (grown to design a new defined culture medium for plant tissue). As this was a time before culture media could be purchased, I nervously weighed out each of the many components. I was greatly relieved when the cultures survived without infection.

While awaiting results of my graduate school applications, I received a telegram from Dr. Robert F. Schilling who had achieved notoriety by developing the test for pernicious anemia at the University of Wisconsin Medical School. He invited me to perform my research for an MS degree in his laboratory, supported by the Wisconsin Alumni Research Foundation. I worked on the binding characteristics of vitamin B12 analogs in gastric juice; binding of the vitamin to a factor secreted in the stomach is deficient in pernicious anemia. An outstanding mentor, he taught me how to write a scientific paper as well as how to conduct an experiment. This work led to an MS degree in Medical Physiology.

But while in this master's program, I was most fortunate to be able to take a cell biology course taught by a renowned scientist, Dr. Hans Ris, a faculty member in the Zoology Department at UW and one of the first to realize that DNA is in a coiled configuration. During one of the laboratory exercises, he showed us the electron microscope; viewing the images therein was love at first sight! (I believe that this was the second electron microscope in the U.S.; we had to hammer the lenses into place!) Studying tissue in the electron microscope presented the opportunity to combine my artistic proclivity with scientific investigation. I then began to think about earning a PhD. Dr. Ris became my mentor although he had never worked with nervous tissue. He was gender blind with the consequence that I never regarded myself as a woman graduate student who might face discrimination later. His standards for excellence were the highest, providing me with lifelong expertise and success in and love of electron microscopy.

What to work on? Another major influence was in the offing. While taking some courses in the medical school for my PhD, I often noticed a tall and lanky guy sitting at the other end of the first row in the lecture hall. It was this person who came to the Schilling laboratory for a summer project. His work necessitated working in the cold room most of the time before heading to the hospital cafeteria at 5:00 to wash dishes. He needed to earn the money required to attend medical school. I thought, "This guy needs some fresh air." Accordingly, I invited him to go sailing on Lake Mendota; I was a member of the Outing Club with access to small sail boats. And this is how Richard P. Bunge and I became acquainted, encouraged by often being becalmed in the middle of the lake!

As a means for funding his medical education, he initially attended medical school half time and worked in a laboratory in the Anatomy Department the rest of the time. His mentor asked him to examine adult cat spinal cord histologically after inserting a needle into the cisterna magna, removing some cerebrospinal fluid, returning it, and repeating this several times (CSF barbotage). His mentor had been doing this to introduce anesthesia and noticed that the cats stumbled but then recovered within a few weeks. This task led to Richard's first discovery that was unexpected and revolutionary; demyelination and subsequent remyelination occurred in the adult mammalian central nervous system. Because there were many details that eluded examination by light microscopy, it made sense for me to continue this tissue analysis in the electron microscope. This became my PhD thesis project. By then we had married leading to both a most satisfactory marital and scientific collaboration.

Many details were revealed in the "big eye" such as the identification of central glia and the mechanism of myelin formation, both controversial topics at the time. This work launched our careers. Upon publication of our results in 1960 and 1961, we received our first invitation to present our findings at an international meeting in Germany. That was an incredible experience, in part because it was the first time in Europe for both of us. We also traveled to France and Italy, setting a pattern for the rest of our professional lives: exploring areas outside our country for one or more days after the invited lectures were done and the meeting concluded. In considering scientific research as a career, I had never thought of it as providing a way to see the world but it did with many invitations throughout the rest of my career.

In 1960, with the MD and PhD degrees, respectively, in hand, we set out for Manhattan to work at Columbia University College of Physicians and Surgeons. It was Richard's aim to learn nerve tissue culture from the master, in this case Dr. Margaret R. Murray who was one of the founders of this field. I would work in an electron microcopy laboratory, in part to link it with Dr. Murray's laboratory; the fine structure of nervous tissue in culture was yet to be delineated. Dr. Murray's team had achieved the first myelination by Schwann cells in culture in 1955, a landmark showing that considerable differentiation could be achieved reliably outside the living organism. I documented that synapses in spinal cord could form in culture. We could walk to work. We have lived close to work for most of our professional lives, particularly important with young children in the family. A long commute robs one of precious time in the lab.

It was in this Columbia period that I discovered the connection between the central nervous system glial cell and the myelin sheath that it formed during development. Having discovered that myelin was reformed in the adult mammal, the question arose if the pattern of remyelination resembled that of its first formation. Scrutinizing kitten spinal cord, I found that it was similar. That it is the oligodendrocyte that forms central myelin and that the cell can form myelin around more than one axon at a time, distinct from the peripheral nervous system, was demonstrated. This was summarized in a drawing that has appeared in many histology textbooks. These findings helped to settle the controversies that had marked central glial cell identification and myelination thus far. This discovery was one of my "Aha" moments in research, a wonderful moment that counters memories of days or weeks or months of repetitive work. To see something for the first time and to answer fundamental questions were the "highs" in research for me, a type of high that continued to drive me for more than half a century in research.

It was during this New York time that we welcomed two sons, Jonathan and Peter, into our family. Thus began the complicated challenge of combining motherhood with a job in science. I held research positions, being funded by Richard's grants obtained as a new Assistant Professor in the Anatomy Department at Columbia's medical school. I did not pursue a full-time faculty position for myself at this time as I could not envision writing grants and preparing lectures at night although I did aim to be productive in research. I worked half time, then 2/3 and finally ¾ time until the younger son entered first grade. And even then I left the lab early to be at home when they returned from school but would often go back to the lab after dinner when Richard then took the helm at home. Later, living close to the lab in St Louis made this possible. Sacrifices were made to concentrate on child rearing and lab work. It is my strong opinion that a working mother cannot have it all "… at the same time," as Michele Obama expressed it recently in a TV interview.

In 1968 to 1969 we spent a sabbatical year in the Department of Neuroscience at Harvard Medical School. A young man, Dr. Dennis Bray, working in the laboratories of Drs. D. Potter and E. Furshpan, was studying sympathetic neurons in culture. As the processes emerged and lengthened from the neuronal cell body, they were tipped by large growth cones seeking new territory. These cones called for close examination; little was known about their content at that time. Some were caught in motion, in order to observe the content of the moving structure. Electron microscopic examination was needed to detect the panoply of organelles contained within the growth cone, including actin filaments. Great patience was needed to slice these diaphanous structures thin enough, and in parallel with their culture substratum, to be resolved in the electron microscope. The growth cone was only present in 3-5 slices; its thinner leading edge was present in only one! A misstep could lead to the loss of that carefully prepared growth cone! The images were among the first obtained for neurite growth cones.

In 1970, offers to join the faculty of the Department of Anatomy and Neurobiology at Washington University School of Medicine were enthusiastically accepted. Richard set up a new tissue culture facility and, with the collaboration of Dr. Patrick Wood, greatly simplified the culture regimens that he had learned in New York. Accordingly, we were then able to study interactions between the cells of peripheral nerve: the Schwann cells, fibroblasts and dorsal root ganglion neurons by culturing these purified populations singly or in various combinations. These cultures enabled discovery of numerous "conversations" that occur among these cell types, thereby providing valuable new information about Schwann cell biology. Electron microscopy was again key for these studies. The fact that there is a mitogenic signal on the surface of axons that causes the Schwann cell to divide was revealed. The importance of extracellular matrix for Schwann cell function was recognized for the first time. The 19-year period in St. Louis was very productive and an exceptional experience in an outstanding academic environment with well attended seminars on Saturday mornings when both basic and clinical researchers could attend.

We wondered how we could translate these basic findings to benefit humans with neurological disease or injury. The answer came in 1988. In 1975, Richard had proposed that the populations of Schwann cells purified in culture could be used for nervous system repair. As Schwann cells were known to be responsible for repair in the peripheral nervous system, why not introduce them into the central nervous system? Schwann cell transplantation experiments began in St. Louis but it soon became apparent that an infrastructure that we did not have was needed. So the offers for Richard to become Scientific Director of the Miami Project to Cure Paralysis and for me to be a Professor of Cell Biology and Neurological Surgery at the University of Miami School of Medicine were welcomed in spite of our Washington University peers (in 1988) looking aghast and asking, "You are going where, to do what?" But as Richard agreed with Goethe's admonition that when the harbor feels safe, it is time to leave, we left in 1989!

Working at the Miami Project enabled Richard's vision of 1975 to become a reality. The Project provided the village that was needed to carry out the many labor intensive transplantation experiments that required cell preparation, surgery, spinal cord injury, animal care, behavioral analysis, neuroanatomical tracing, and numerous methods to evaluate the tissue weeks or months after the transplantation. Transplanted Schwann cells were discovered to improve outcome after spinal cord injury. The use of a rat contusion model mirrored the spinal cord injury in humans; the complete transection model allowed us to demonstrate with certainty that axons regenerated into the Schwann cell implant. The work went on despite Richard's passing in 1996 and my dedication to the Miami Project as Interim Scientific Director for a year. The nearly 30 years of work in my laboratory showed that the Schwann cells were more effective when combined with another treatment such as the introduction of growth factors; Schwann cells transduced with a virus to generate neurotrophins led to improved cell survival after transplantation and more axonal growth into the transplant.

In 2007, a group of us at the Project started meeting weekly to generate a plan to prepare an application to the FDA for approval to test autologous Schwann cell transplantation in a clinical trial for subjects with subacute spinal cord injuries. The considerable amount of data generated in our lab and by others in the Project gave us confidence that we were justified in doing so. The application was submitted in September 2011 and, after providing responses to FDA concerns, was approved in July 2012. The procedures to acquire the Schwann cells from a peripheral nerve biopsy from the subject, stimulate the cells to increase in number in culture, and transplant them into the spinal cord injury site were found to be feasible and safe. Also half the subjects recovered some conduction through the injury site. A second autologous Schwann cell trial for those with chronic spinal cord injury is underway. Thus we have been most fortunate to have experienced a "bench to bedside" journey over many years.

What has contributed to enabling this journey? As an only child, spending time alone observing nature and accomplishing creative projects fostered inspiration, creativity, and independence. Enrolling in an outstanding summer program while in college opened up new vistas. Performing work that generated beautiful images was fulfilling in that, in my case, achieving artistic photographs enabled me to express my artistic capabilities along with acquiring important scientific data. Choosing two gender blind and talented mentors during graduate school assured confidence and a quest for excellence. Having confidence is important for the risk taking that is needed to investigate new paths. Also, choosing outstanding trainees to work in the laboratory is crucial to generate high quality work. But for me, most important was to find a highly gifted and compatible, 40-year collaborator who shared my passion for the work that was performed in our laboratory.

Acknowledgments

The author is most grateful for the long, enjoyable, inspired and successful partnership with Richard P. Bunge, M.D.; the unique, valuable and also long term collaboration with Patrick M. Wood, PhD, and Margaret L. Bates who followed the Bunges to Florida; Dr. Naomi Kleitman who also accompanied the Bunges to Miami to make key and multiple contributions to the laboratory; the many talented and productive students and fellows; and loyal and dedicated assistants. Productivity in the Miami period was buoyed by the research environment created in the Miami Project to Cure Paralysis by the Scientific Directors, R. P. Bunge (1989-1996) and W. Dalton Dietrich, PhD (1997-present); generous funding from the Miami Project and the Buoniconti Fund also was key. Forty-five years of continuous funding from the National Institute of Neurological Disorders and Stroke (NINDS) of the National Institutes of Health is appreciatively acknowledged. Twenty years of funding from the Christopher and Dana Reeve Foundation provided valuable support for our work. ■

Gauri Agarwal, MD, FACP

Associate Dean for Clinical Curriculum
University of Miami Miller School of Medicine

My mother was born in a small rural village in southern India. She lived at the base of a mountain among jackfruit and guava trees in a thatch-roofed hut. She awoke every morning to draw water from a well, pour the water into a large copper pot, and heat it with fire. She would use a tumbler to take small amounts of the water and bathe outdoors while chickens clucked by her side. She was one of six children and had lost her father due to a heart attack. When he died, he was only in his forties and she was four years old. He was conscious and alert when he stumbled from the fields clutching his chest, but by the time a rickshaw arrived to carry him to the nearest medical facility, he had passed. My grandmother survived with the meager earnings of their farming and the generosity of neighbors. However, the rainy season would often drench the fields and money would be scarce. These are the times my mother remembers – the hunger, the minimal oil left to light a lamp at night, and her mother's face worn with grief.

Going to school in such times was an act of heroism but my grandmother insisted that all her children continue their education. My mother would walk with her younger brother, holding his hand as they navigated around poinciana trees, a wandering water buffalo, and the occasional cobra. School was a respite. She absorbed every word and valued every fact. Her teachers commented on her ability to learn quickly and encouraged her to take the national exams that could allow her to earn a college scholarship. She was also a gifted runner. She competed in track and field at a time in India when women were expected to wear long wide skirts, even while running. She decided to cut the skirt down the middle and sewed them back together into pants. I imagine my mother as a young teenage girl jumping hurdles in palazzo pants. Although she was not the eldest son of the family, she was supported by my grandmother who recognized her unique talent and ability. She earned her scholarship which covered tuition and rooming but nothing else. Her other expenses would have to be funded by other means. My grandmother scraped every thing she could spare to pay for my mother's bus ticket. She travelled alone with exactly two sets of clothes. Upon arriving in the town where the college was located, she realized she had no place to live and asked a family if she could stay in their attic in exchange for cooking and cleaning. She survived this way until her first scholarship check arrived.

Every day, she purchased a small bowl of rice and lentils which she divided into two meals. She studied every moment she could, excelled, and was offered a scholarship to medical school. Just prior to her final year of medical school, at the age of 20, her older brother said there was someone the family thought she should meet. She met a young man who was leaving shortly for Washington University in St. Louis to complete a PhD in engineering. By all accounts, he was brilliant, kind, and of their caste. Their marriage was arranged after their first meeting and they left shortly after for the U.S. Medical school remained unfinished and all her hard work was left in India. My older sister was born shortly after that and I was born eight years later. During those years, my father encouraged my mother to return to her studies and she completed her master's degree. In 1978, they decided they missed their families and my father had an excellent opportunity to teach at the Indian Institute of Science in Bangalore, India. They returned home, and this time, my mother decided to go back to medical school. Her medical school was a ten-hour train ride away, but my father encouraged her, and she would leave for months at a time to complete her degree. I can remember holding her leg and crying at the train station as she tried to board. She returned after attaining her medical degree and began practicing internal medicine at a hospital in Bangalore. We stayed in India until 1984 when my father was offered a university position in Florida. My mother focused on ensuring my sister and I adjusted well to a new life in America. She decided her medical career was over as the process of retaking exams and repeating a residency at that stage in her life seemed a Sisyphean task. My father again encouraged her, and she studied for her exams and earned a position in a pediatric residency program at Miami Children's Hospital. As a young girl, I saw her awaken at dawn to prepare and leave meals for the family and then drive an hour from our home in Boca Raton to Miami, often returning very late in the evening. She completed her residency and is now in her seventies, still taking care of young children in pediatric emergency rooms. Often, she is still there at 4 AM, long after her shift ended at 12 AM because she can't bear to leave a sick child once she has begun treating them. In those years of her residency training, my sister and I learned to be independent. At the age of seven, I took the school bus home, used my key to enter my home, made a snack, and watched Knight Rider and cartoons until I heard my father come home. I would immediately turn the television off and get to my homework. My sister came from India to the U.S. as a sophomore in high school and navigated the cultural divide with surprising ease. She mastered every subject, became the captain of the debate team, yearbook editor, and was accepted to Harvard. Mirroring my mother's life, she flew by herself to Boston, insisting she needed no help to move into her dorm. She travelled the world after college working with the World Bank in Germany, Russia, and Outer Mongolia. She went back to Harvard for business school and now lives in London as a hedge fund manager and runs her own foundation supporting major global health projects.

I begin by sharing the stories of the women in my family as they are stories of resilience, independence, and determination. I grew up with the privilege of not experiencing hunger and was able to go to school with every resource needed to succeed in a smooth and straight path. I watched my mother in India and America administering to patients and holding young infants, and fell in love with medicine. I worked hard and earned admission to the University of Miami (UM) Six Year Honors Program in Medicine. I was committed to meeting the benchmark set by the women in my family and remember doing well until I took a death and dying course. I wrote a 20-page paper on Sati, the ancient practice of wives self-immolating on the funeral pyre of their husbands. I thought I had done a fabulous job. I received a B+ on the paper because it didn't fit the thesis statement structure sought by my professor and so I received an A- in the class. I met with the professor to argue my point and begged to have a chance to revise the paper. He stared at me – a teenage girl who was already guaranteed admission to medical school sitting there arguing about a grade – and said one day, I would look back at this moment and be embarrassed. He was entirely correct.

I began medical school at the age of eighteen and quickly realized that I was not as prepared as the older, more experienced students who had spent at least four years as undergraduates preparing for the rigor of medical school. I spectacularly crashed and burned in biochemistry which was humbling for someone who had turned my nose up at an A-. I went through the classic phase of considering myself an imposter among intellectual giants and that feeling persisted for my first two years of medical school. In my third year, everything changed when I began my clerkships. As I spent my days with individuals who were truly suffering, looking to me and my team for answers, I remembered why I was there. I would spend hours at the bedside talking, laughing, reassuring, answering questions, and looking at family photos. I remember a moment in my surgery clerkship when I was partnered with two other students who were intent on pursuing surgery as a career. We were on the pancreaticobiliary service and my assigned patient had a pancreatic mass. He was scheduled for a Whipple and was understandably anxious. I spent an hour reading poetry to him from his favorite anthology and discussing the upcoming surgery. My fellow students thought this was bizarre and relentlessly teased me, but I had discovered something that reinvigorated my drive and renewed my purpose.

It was during my medicine clerkship that I found my calling and had a senior resident who embodied the kind of physician I aspired to become. She was brilliant, kind, witty, and carried herself with a quiet strength and confidence. I followed her like a duckling, absorbing every motion of her hand during a lumbar puncture and every intonation of her voice while speaking to a patient. The patients we saw were incredibly interesting and I fell in love with the intellectual challenge of internal medicine. I also met my husband at the end of my medicine clerkship. He was a visiting internal medicine resident from another program, and we were sharing a patient I had transferred to the ICU. He helped me with my residency application process, and I travelled the country searching for my program. I loved the training program at Northwestern in Chicago, but I knew my husband was inclined to stay in Florida to be closer to family. As we sat down trying to come up with my ultimate rank list, he told me in a soft voice the next phase of our life should be based on where I believed I would receive the best training and he would support any decision. We ended up at Northwestern and it was a year of my first job, marriage, and living away from family, all at the age of 22. It was an incredibly challenging year to navigate so many learning curves and new responsibilities.

At the end of that year, my husband decided that he wanted to continue radiation oncology training and was able to secure a position at the University of Pittsburgh. We realized quickly that Pittsburgh was quite a distance from Chicago, so I decided it was my time to sacrifice. I met with my program director who was understandably disappointed but immediately picked up the phone and secured a position for me, also at the University of Pittsburgh. I will always remain grateful for his kindness and support. We moved to Pittsburgh and loved the city, the program, and our new friends. We had our first son there during my chief residency year and I stayed on as faculty while my husband finished his last year of training. I had always enjoyed teaching and was honored to be chosen for a leadership position. I had thought my whole career would be spent in clinical practice. I imagined there would be nothing more gratifying than serving patients and families at their moment of greatest need. However, it was during my chief residency year that I had profound and career changing insight. I realized by teaching medical students and residents, I could have a deep and early impact on their approach to patients, career choice, and practice style. I realized the multiplier effect of teaching allows a teacher to not only impact her own patients, but also the patients of every one of her students.

We decided to move to Boston while my husband was doing a one-year fellowship at Massachusetts General Hospital, and I joined the clinical teaching faculty at Beth Israel Deaconess. While in Boston, our second son was born. Having two boys under the age of three was a blessing and an extraordinary challenge. I was blessed to have a nanny and a flexible schedule but missed being close to family. Both my husband and I were offered long-term positions but decided our goal to have our children grow up close to their grandparents was more important. I was concerned whether I could find an academic position in Boca Raton where my parents lived and where we wanted to settle. I reached out to my department chair in Boston who connected me to a dean at UM. He mentioned they were starting a Regional Medical Campus in Boca Raton. He didn't think there would be any opportunities, but I sent an email anyway. My email ended up reaching a man who would turn out to be one of the most influential figures in my life, Dr. Daniel Lichtstein. Dr. Lichtstein interviewed me and offered me a full-time position at the campus to help develop a new curriculum that UM was piloting. It was an incredibly exciting task to research innovations in medical education and build a curriculum that included very intense and early patient exposure in the first year of medical school, small mentoring learning communities, a strong problem-based learning curriculum, integrated clinical clerkships, medical simulation, and low faculty to student ratios. In 2009, Dr. Lichtstein offered me an assistant dean position and I was promoted to an associate dean in 2015. Throughout the years I worked with him, he has been incredibly supportive of the need to balance my work with the other commitments in my life. He understood when the other junior faculty and I brought our children to the office when they were off from school or when we had to pick them up in the middle of the day because of vague abdominal pain. When I was pregnant with my twin girls, I went into premature labor and was placed on bedrest for two months. I was entirely capable of working via phone and email, and he allowed me that privilege for two months. There are many adages about the inability of women to work together and I have never found that to be true. My closest colleagues, a team of primarily women faculty, have been my closest friends, colleagues, and confidantes. Balance is an elusive word and it is made infinitely easier when working with a wonderful and supportive team. I believe seeking this balance is the most critical piece when considering a career prospect. Who will you be working with and who will be your mentor?

Our decision to live close to family has also been critical for my children's development and the support I have received – the infinite number of pickups, drop-offs, meals, and other acts of kindness from our parents are priceless. I also had no guilt in hiring an incredible woman as a nanny. She would help me wake up my children, get them dressed, prepare breakfast, drive them to school, run errands, grab groceries, drop off dry cleaning, run the dishwasher and the laundry, prep for dinner, and help with driving the children to after school activities. She became an essential component of my family and I trusted her with my life for seven years. Ultimately, she had to move to Connecticut, and my husband and I have been able to manage everything on our own as the children grew up. I am a busy full-time dean with many side projects but when I'm with my children, I'm focused on them. I help with homework, I drive them to their activities, I show up at events, and I make mom jokes. The relationship with my husband also needs to be supported and we have Friday night date nights – sacrosanct time away from work, responsibilities, the children, or other worries during which we can talk as partners who enjoy each other's company.

If a moment of guilt crops up about being away from the children, I try to remember a distinct moment when I was scheduled to speak to my older son's kindergarten class. As I walked into the room, he said with delight, "That's my mommy. She's a doctor!" I was taken aback by his pride and happiness and recognized that my sons will see the capabilities of women and I will model a path for my daughters that they can do this, too. My family's story is about resilient and strong women, but my story also includes encouraging and supportive men. We alternate leaning on one another. My wish and advice for young women who are beginning their life in medicine is enjoy the privilege of a life well-lived in the service of others. Whether most of your day is spent in direct patient care, research, teaching, administrative work, or mothering, it is in the service of others. In challenging times, find strength and joy in that purpose. Whenever I have needed a resurgence of resilience, I think of my mother as a young girl – fatherless, hungry, and bathing outside in well water. For some reason, knowing her, and despite the circumstances, I always imagine her as a girl with a smile on her face, enjoying the warmth of the water and enjoying the beauty of the surrounding guava trees. ▨

Ellen Faye Barrett, PhD

Professor of Physiology & Biophysics
University of Miami Miller School of Medicine

I spent my first three years on a farm in eastern Oregon with my mother and maternal grandmother, while my father was overseas in the U.S. Army during World War II. My mother, an excellent student, had not been allowed to attend college because her family thought she was already "smart enough." She was determined to send her children to college so they would have a profession. All three of us graduated from the University of Washington, and we created a UW scholarship fund in our parents' names targeting students from a rural background who are the first in their family to attend college.

When my father left the Army, he had a job in a lumber company and our family moved to Seattle. He and my grandfather built our house. My sister was born when I was almost four, and my brother two years later. We had enough money to live, but little extra. The few books and records we owned were played and read over and over. I still have four books of poetry from my paternal grandmother (a former teacher). I read the monthly *Reader's Digest* practically cover to cover plus the *Ladies Home Journal.* We caught many of the childhood diseases that vaccines now prevent (measles, chicken pox, mumps) and I remember my mother's happiness when the Salk polio vaccine became available.

We walked 10 blocks to elementary school, without worries about safety. I remember a wonderful junior high social studies teacher (the first black person I had ever met), and a science teacher I idolized. There was social pressure against being smart – students offered to pay me not to do well on exams. In the tenth grade I was awarded a scholarship to a private girl's high school, a transformative experience. There were dedicated teachers, small classes, discussions of history and literature, essay exams, and summer reading lists.

I was accepted at Stanford, Pomona, and the University of Washington (UW). I enrolled at UW for financial reasons, beginning as a chemistry major, but after a year switched to psychology. My all-girl high school had offered no math classes beyond geometry/algebra and making up the math classes required for a physics class would have taken an extra year. And it was clear that many of the chemistry department faculty did not like women!

I especially liked physiological psychology. My senior research rotation mentors, a professor and his postdoctoral fellow, were good and kind. The postdoc was amazingly patient with a lab newbie – I once missed an experiment because I thought Valentine's Day was an official holiday! I earned the opportunity to add my name as co-author to my first scientific paper (concerning the electrophysiology of vision in cats) and got accepted to graduate schools in psychology (though one professor agreed to write a recommendation only if I promised to never get married). I graduated in 1966 as the president's medalist, with fellowship offers from Danforth, Woodrow Wilson, and the National Science Foundation. But then I switched majors again, because my insightful research mentor professor noticed I liked physiology more than psychology and advised me to apply to the physiology and biophysics graduate program and work with a newly hired professor. This turned out to be excellent advice.

I had wanted to apply to medical school, but the University's official pre-medical advisor, whom I consulted early in my undergraduate years, said if I had never stayed up all night, I was an unsuitable candidate for medical school. (I later discovered that she discouraged all women and thought only sons of doctors should attend medical school.) Later when I joined the faculty at the University of Miami, I took great pleasure in serving on a committee that changed the practice of having the dean's administrative aide (who also did not favor women doctors) select the medical school applications to be reviewed by the admissions committee. Currently, the abundance and diversity of women in UM medical school classes is wonderful to see.

The physiology and biophysics graduate program provided excellent training. In a year long pro-seminar course, every week we read five to ten assigned research papers and then discussed them with a faculty expert, which gave us a broad knowledge of physiology concepts. The course ended in June with a mega exam week, which included three eight-hour days answering essay questions. My husband-to-be, John Barrett, a fellow graduate student who had taken the exam a year earlier, coached me over the weeks leading to the exam, and his help was invaluable, because many professors asked the same questions every year!

John and I married in the turbulent year of 1968, and I began my research project, which involved electrophysiological recordings from frog neuromuscular junctions. The recordings were super-sensitive to vibrations, so during experiments we placed "Out of Order" signs on the restroom next door!

After I collected all the data for my dissertation, our daughter Jeannie was born in 1971. We couldn't afford childcare, so I stayed home and wrote my dissertation and research papers (and parts of John's) during her naps. Later I learned some physiology faculty wanted to expel me for being pregnant, but my mentor supported me. In 1972, John and I defended our dissertations and by that time he had completed a year of postdoctoral research.

We both applied for NIH postdoctoral fellowships in different cities. John graciously offered to postpone his postdoctoral work so I could work at the University of Colorado in Denver (UC). At UC Denver I worked with two established and an up-and-coming investigators in my field and completed a small project. John found another position in Denver working on a difficult project with an equally difficult mentor. Several scientists criticized him for postponing his postdoctoral work for me. Later he said helping me stay in science was one of the best decisions he ever made. Concurrently the federal government instituted a new policy requiring universities that received government funding to hire more women faculty. I was offered an assistant professor position in the zoology department at the University of Iowa (UI). The UI kindly agreed to hold my job for seven months, so John could do postdoctoral work to learn neuronal cell culture at Harvard's Neurobiology Department.

We drove in two separate vehicles from Denver via Iowa to Boston, I drove a car with our daughter, and John drove a U-Haul truck with all our possessions. This was a crazy adventure only young people would undertake, since there were no cell phones and he had the only map! John learned neuronal cell culture, and we moved to Iowa, where he began postdoctoral research in another department, with the promise of a faculty position a year later.

In Iowa my first assignment was teaching a course in comparative physiology, a real challenge, since I had previously studied only vertebrate physiology. I got a big textbook on insects, read a chapter each night and taught it the next day! Fortunately, most of the students in the course were premeds and didn't mind learning mostly about vertebrates. Unfortunately, the zoology department was the most sexist workplace I've experienced. The (male) leader of the neuroscience group displayed a poster with a full-length nude woman above his desk. Women graduate students were used as cheap labor/teaching assistants for their first two years, then given a difficult qualifying exam they would all fail. No one had ever counselled or warned these women about the mass fail-out exam. And the chairman reneged on his earlier promise that I could teach one semester, then have the other semester free to do research.

We wrote a Christmas card to our fellow graduate student Karl Magleby, a new assistant professor in the physiology and biophysics department at the University of Miami, telling him we were looking for different jobs. Long story short, in 1974 we were hired as assistant professors. Fortunately for us, at that time, NIH grants were relatively easier to win, and you only had to be awarded one grant to make UM happy. John got spectacular results with two of his early lab projects, and in 1978 we were both awarded tenure – a real blessing.

During our first year in Miami we rented a house in little Havana and tried to learn something about life in the Southeast before buying a house. We learned old pine trees mark the highest ground, and the roof shape best for withstanding hurricane winds. In 1975, shortly before the birth of our younger daughter, we bought an old house for $60,000 in Coral Gables within walking distance of UM's main campus and West Lab Elementary School, and near the train tracks that years later became Metrorail.

It was difficult to raise two children while working full-time. John worked very long hours, basically running both labs. I served a four-year term on Neurology A study section (I was the second female member), where I learned that John's and my salaries were very low. I learned we had been hired at a two-for-the-price-of-one salary. After receiving job offers from another university, we were able to persuade UM to raise our salaries a bit. In later years I served on another NIH study section for program project grants, and then on the editorial board of the *Journal of Physiology*. These outside responsibilities were good for my career but put an extra strain on my family. I am so grateful for the kind and generous nature of my husband and our daughters.

The Physiology and Biophysics Department has considerable teaching responsibilities in the medical curriculum. Because the department had many neuroscientists, my first chairman told me to select another physiology subject to teach. I chose the kidney and was mentored by several kind MDs and nephrologists. I once taught GI and endocrine physiology and now also teach respiratory physiology with my current chairman, Karl Magleby. At first all basic sciences were taught together in the MS1 year. Later the MS2 curriculum was reorganized into organ system modules, with basic and clinical lectures grouped together. I liked this arrangement and learned a great deal from pulmonologist Matthias Salathe and nephrologist Warren Kupin about making our physiology presentations relevant and helpful to medical students. In recent years I also coordinated the physiology section of the cellular function and regulation course, finally getting to teach neuroscience! In courses I teach, students receive (in addition to PowerPoint lectures) written lecture notes, study Q & A, and practice exams. We also send congratulatory letters to students who perform especially well. I have served for many years on curriculum steering committees. Students have awarded me Paff Teaching and Unsung Hero Awards, for which I am grateful.

I have also taught neuroscience and cell biology in graduate student courses and was a founding member of the graduate neuroscience program.

A mentor suggested I try to serve on "power" committees to learn the internal administration of the medical school. I served on the appointments, promotion and tenure committee (including a year as chair) and the scientific awards committee that dispenses intramural funds to support research.

For many years I was part of a research team with John Barrett, an innovator with the imagination and persistence to make difficult experiments work; Gabriel David, a careful thinker and excellent, organized experimentalist; and I was the writer who helped pull everything together into papers. We demonstrated the abundant mitochondria in motor nerve terminals provide not only ATP but also temporary sequestration of entering calcium loads, and mitochondrial dysfunction is an early event in motor neuron degenerative disease. Dr. David was originally a postdoctoral fellow in the lab. He eventually became a faculty member, but UM's rules, that (in my opinion) overemphasize independence, broke up our team, and we lost a fine researcher and teacher to early retirement.

In 2007, at age 62, I was diagnosed with Stage IIIC uterine papillary serous carcinoma, ~30% chance of five-year survival. The four-month delay between noticing symptoms and getting the diagnosis was a frustrating ordeal. I was well treated by Dr. Matt Pearson, and a psychologist and nurses at Sylvester Cancer Center, with surgery, radiation and multiple rounds of both intravenous and intraperitoneal chemotherapy. Happily, the tumor marker fell rapidly during the chemo treatment and to this date has never increased. I was fortunate to be able to continue working throughout (albeit at a reduced pace) with supportive colleagues, students, and family. John researched the cancer, planned the extra intraperitoneal chemotherapy with my doctor, let me talk about the cancer whenever I needed to, and remained hopeful throughout. In 2010, a routine follow-up PET/CT scan disclosed an active spot in a lung, which fortunately was not a metastasis but rather a typical carcinoid, surgically cured by a middle lobectomy. After these medical experiences, questions about renal protection during chemotherapy and the shunt created during lung resections have appeared in medical student problem sets! I was so fortunate to receive excellent medical care and to have comprehensive medical insurance coverage, and to survive to see our daughters and grandchildren as they live their adventures.

These cancers, though successfully treated, have made the transient nature of life very clear. I have become much less tolerant of B.S. and more willing to speak my mind. I have served on the Faculty Senate and Medical Faculty Council as they deal with troubling issues raised by budgetary constraints and changes in leadership. It is good to see women's issues (leadership, salary inequities, family leave, harassment) receiving more attention, though much remains to be done. I have worked hard but have also been blessed with abundant good fortune.

Words of wisdom:
You can't do everything, at least not all at once, so set priorities.

Choose a life partner who is fully supportive of your work

Good mentors come in both genders.

Study men's & women's conversational styles (e.g. "You Just Don't Understand" by Deborah Tannen) to cope in a male-dominated workplace.

An act of kindness or courage can reap surprising benefits, even years later.

Serve on committees that teach you important things and produce positive results.

Find and work with people whose strengths complement your own.

If you encounter problems, report them to people who have the power to fix them. ■

Monica M. Yepes, MD

Associate Professor of Radiology
Chief, Breast Imaging
Director of Breast Imaging Services
University of Miami Miller School of Medicine

My father, a psychiatrist, was my greatest role model. He taught me to regard working with people to relieve their pain and suffering as not only a career choice but as a moral calling. I never questioned whether I should pursue medicine as it was natural with his encouragement. As the eldest of only two daughters, I was taught the importance of having a work ethic, and how to be driven and focused to settle for no less than excellence. My father had blazed his own trail from extraordinarily humble beginnings. He was born in a small town in the Colombian Andes mountains and managed to graduate first in his class from one of the country's elite medical schools in Medellin. He graduated with two specialties, first in Colombia in pediatrics, and the second from New York State University in psychiatry. Upon returning to Colombia he became president of the Colombian Association of Psychiatry and co-founded the Colombian Biologic Psychiatric Association. Therefore, I was expected to achieve more since I came from more affluence than he did.

Although I was also born in Colombia, I was brought to the U.S. at the age of 9 months, and approximately 10 years later, our family returned to Colombia. My parents had always planned to return to their homeland to raise their daughters. When we went back to Colombia in the late 1970s, I was traumatized and perceived my country as quaint and uncivilized compared to the U.S. Nevertheless, the comfort of our extended families and their support and the excellent American school I attended created a smooth transition. I adapted and flourished as a bi-cultural student.

My father supported my decision to study medicine. He always believed medicine to be a noble pursuit and a rewarding life choice. He was a feminist and wanted me to have a fulfilling career so I could thrive and live independently. My mother, a dedicated home maker for whom raising two daughters provided a lifetime of joy and sacrifice, wanted me to pursue a career other than "the home." With both of my parents' encouragement I believed I could aspire to be anything I wanted.

In my class of 80 medical students, I was one of only 15 female students. Among my classmates, in our state of Antioquia, I placed first and ranked third in the national interns' examination. I loved my career choice and the work I did, and never regretted the sacrifice and hard work. Although, I never anticipated the impact the patients' pain and suffering would have on me. I had not realized after many years watching my mother's battle with chronic illness how her suffering diminished my capacity to deal with the patients' pain. I loved the challenge of studying medicine and could never imagine myself on any other path, but I realized the emotional toll was significant.

During my national mandatory general practice year in a level 1 hospital, I became attracted to the rapidly-evolving field of radiology. I realized the field served my need to understand the "why" of disease processes by providing me with a logical system of disease pattern recognition with less direct exposure to the outcomes. The advent of this new technology coupled with the promise of its development to pinpoint the cause of a patient's symptoms, won me over. Yet once in residency, despite all my rationalizations, I still desired patient contact so I could minimize their difficult journeys through illness. During my residency, with guidance from my professors and mentors, I realized women's health imaging, and specifically breast imaging, gave me the opportunity to combine my desire to improve human health and reduce the stress of tests and procedures involved in diagnosing breast cancer.

After completing my observerships in Miami and Spain, I began to establish my Medellin, Colombia-based practice in radiology. I had married my husband Juan, who was my rock and best friend. While he always dreamed of moving to the U.S. in search of better opportunities, I assumed it would be difficult to transfer my career to America. As Colombia's political and social challenges continued to deteriorate along with concern for the safety of our children, I accepted a breast imaging fellowship at the University of Miami.

In 2001 at the age of 34, I moved to Miami with my husband and two young children to start over again. A year later when I completed my fellowship, I was fortunate to be offered an alternate pathway to accreditation for foreign radiologists and was appointed UM assistant professor of breast imaging. Over the next four years I adapted to this new culture and achieved board certification from the American Board of Radiology. Our family was granted U.S. citizenship, which increased our sense of belonging to this very generous and gracious country.

The very delicate balance of pursuing an academic and clinical career, while adapting to a new culture and being a wife *and* mother of two small children was not easy. As I spent many hours studying for boards, while my children begged to just sit in the room with me promising to "be quiet" I was filled with guilt and concern. Had I made the right choice? Should I go back to Colombia where I already had established my professional life and not put them through this? None of my achievements could have been possible without immense and unwavering support of my incredible husband who put his career on hold while the children were young. In moments of doubt when my instinct was to turn and flee, he reminded me of the future and the opportunities and safety we could provide our family by persisting. It was only after I completed my recertification process and the children were older when he pursued and completed his dream PhD in virtual education.

My greatest advice to young women attempting to thrive in a such a demanding career as medicine, is surround yourselves with partners who believe in you, support you and are willing to make as many sacrifices as you are making. The other equally important caveat is to be kind to yourself. The constant demands of attending to the needs of a partner, children, patients, colleagues, and the need to participate in research, administration, and promotion are overwhelming. We can only achieve all our goals through diligence and hard work and with appropriate mentorship and support from our closest friends and family. And please be patient with yourself and allow some imperfection so you can cope and make it all happen. The goals we expect to achieve in this crazy world are not always quickly attained. You must rely on self-discipline to remain on track and persist.

Throughout my entire adjustment process, I worked to change the highly impersonal practice in which patients rarely got to speak with the radiologist unless a procedure was involved. I chose to use a personal approach by explaining the results to the patient after their diagnostic mammogram, ultrasound, and/or biopsy. Over time I pioneered the UM standard care practice that by minimizing a patient's anxiety while they waited for their results and providing them with an easily understood report, communication between patients and physicians greatly improved as evidenced by my research.

I also derived great satisfaction from teaching medical students and residents. I have taught them how diseases express themselves clinically and through images, so they can see the whole patient separate from their diagnostic image. Students can then fully participate with the clinical team and patients can receive the best possible treatment and clinical outcomes. I also teach students to speak with patients, inquire about their medical past and family history to assess their breast cancer risk factors, and refer them, when appropriate, to genetic counseling to tailor their screening tests. I have tried to impress upon students that a good breast imager must get out from behind the viewing station and interact with the patient, and it is our responsibility to honestly and hopefully convey both good and bad news. But above all, I teach students to be compassionate in every patient interaction no matter how small or insignificant.

In 2007, I was awarded the Henry H. Lerner Teaching Award, and named fellowship director. Over the years I actively mentored residents to complete their research requirements; two were awarded the Mark Shapiro Award for Excellence. Many of the residents also presented at national meetings. I authored and participated in multiple publications evaluating imaging biomarkers, imaging characteristics of unusual diseases and the effects of patient communication, including with diverse patient populations.

Thanks to the mentorship and trust of our section chief, Dr. Richard Kiszonas and our chairman, Dr. Robert Quencer, I also worked in the administrative arena. As a Department of Radiology committee member, I've served on the Resident Selection Committee, the Radiology Research Committee, and the Radiology Residency Research Committee, all of which are excellent learning experiences. I believe my participation in our national organizations has fundamentally improved my research. Under Dr. Quencer's mentorship, I became involved in the American College of Radiology's Appropriateness Criteria Committee, an extraordinary learning experience which also provided networking and an understanding of the complex process of creating standards.

In 2011, I was appointed section chief of the breast imaging section. Only two years later, in 2013, my proposal and justification for digital breast tomosynthesis obtained approval. I was also assigned as the point of contact to plan and direct the expansion of Breast Imaging at UMH, Plantation, Jackson Memorial Hospital, and Lennar in Coral Gables. Recently we completed the expansion of the Posner Women's Center which doubled our resources, increased patient accessibility, and raised the number of faculty in our section from three to thirteen.

In addition to working on my career in the U.S., I have always strived to give back to my country of origin, Colombia, and share all I have learned. I maintained my

Colombian professional and academic relationships by extensively lecturing at both local and national Colombia-based conferences and offered my expertise. I have also spoken by invitation in Panama and Mexico. I have always believed our Miami location makes UM a global reference point for Latin America, and I hope we continue to create liaisons for further growth and to improve knowledge in those countries.

Despite my preconception, being a woman has never been an obstacle. I'm exceedingly fortunate to have met and worked with male colleagues who had respect for women and recognize the value of females in general, and specifically in a women's health subspecialty. I believe as female physicians we bring a sense of fairness, justice, and compassion to every interaction which is appreciated by leadership. Nevertheless, it is always important to speak up and be firm, if necessary. Respect is inspired and earned through each of our interactions with our superiors and those whom we lead. My other perceived "handicap" as a Latina (although a very lucky one due to my bi-cultural childhood which assisted my transition) was never an issue, particularly with a diverse patient population, instead it was always an asset. My experience is a tribute to the University of Miami as a consistently diverse workplace. Embracing diversity gave me the chance to model female leadership for our female students and residents from all backgrounds. Watching a woman from a diverse background succeed, even under my own unlikely circumstances, is the best incentive for everyone to embrace their ambition that may otherwise seem unattainable.

My advice is to remember our work is always more meaningful than we think, (yet even more work is necessary to achieve a promotion). Early in your career it is important to identify a good mentor who will selflessly and generously guide you and commit to your path. Never consider your ideas or questions as unworthy of further exploration. If you diligently work to present your ideas in the appropriate venue, you will succeed. There is nothing worse than learning an idea you previously dismissed as unworthy is later presented and lauded as important. Run with your ideas. And remember the journey is more important than your destination because it is on your journey where you set your goals and choose medicine as a career. The accolades and promotions are recognition of your journey, not of a single event.

On the personal side and as a mother, I always worried about the things I missed in my children's lives, and how it affected their development. I always envied my friends who attended all their children's school events and evaluations. And when I was received by other mothers with the words, "Oh! So, you're Veronica's mother!" on the rare occasion when my work scheduled allowed me to attend an event, hearing those words felt like they were pushing a dagger into my heart. And yet, when my daughter grew up and we broached this difficult subject (for me) she laughed! She assured me she admired and respected my choices and my career accomplishments and those of our family. She credited her growth as a strong independent woman who could aspire to anything due to watching me accomplish so much. Another rewarding moment was when I was asked to present at my son's third-grade class for career day. He was mortified and assumed I would talk about breasts! He made me promise I would not acknowledge him, and much less embarrass him by kissing or hugging him. I carefully respected his request, yet when I finished my presentation (which of course was not just about breasts) and he saw his classmates truly enjoyed it, he ran up in front of his entire class and hugged and kissed me. And as he grew up and I apologized for not being like most of his friends' mothers because I had missed so many of his events, he proudly said, "Mom, what are you talking about? You were saving lives." My children, both of whom are now adults, tease me and say they were spared a dreaded "helicopter parent" by my choice to pursue a medical career allowing them to become independent. The best testament to my serving as my children's role model is my daughter choosing to also pursue a medical career. And my son, a true feminist, insists his wife will have a meaningful career to also be proud of, which leads me to believe after all my worrying, I successfully raised my two children!

In summary, it is a privilege and an honor to build a career dedicated to the care of women with breast cancer and to play a part in alleviating their pain and suffering. I'm fortunate to have used my bi-cultural background to embrace many women who find it difficult to deal with a life-threatening disease in a foreign culture. I have given back what has been bestowed on me as an American citizen. I have a strong desire to continue to grow and contribute to breast cancer care, education, research, and community service. And I am immensely grateful to have served, and hopefully inspired present and future medical students and residents who will embark on such a rewarding life choice.

And remember, always be kind to yourselves! ▨

Marie Denise Gervais, MD

Assistant Dean for Admissions and Diversity
Director, Pre-Doctoral Education
Department of Family Medicine and Community Health
University of Miami Miller School of Medicine.

My parents married in Haiti after my father received his medical diploma in Port-au-Prince and was about to finish his residency in radiology. Afterwards, he immigrated to the U.S. to pursue advanced medical education and was grateful to find a position as a radiology resident in St. Louis, Missouri. My mother joined him in St Louis after the completion of his first year. During my father's last year of residency my twin brother and I were born when our older brother was 13 months old.

In the early 60s, during segregation, many parts of the United States were still segregated, and my parents lived in a predominantly black neighborhood. Often, my father recounted an incident at a restaurant where he and two other black residents decided to have lunch. He described the manager coming to their table and saying they could not be served. When my father, in his heavy Haitian French accent asked why and the manager recognized my father's foreign accent, they were told only my father could stay. The manager would not serve the U.S. citizens because of their skin color. In response, all three men left. My father realized he and my mother could not raise their children in such an environment. As soon as his residency training ended, our young family went back to Port-au-Prince, Haiti to live closer to my grandparents and our huge extended family.

The early 60s marked the beginning of political turmoil and civil insecurity in Haiti with the rise to power of François Duvalier, who appointed himself as President for life. My father could not continue to think his young family would grow in such an unstable environment. At the time French Canada was heavily recruiting French-speaking professionals. My father, a physician, and my mother an elementary school teacher decided to move to Montreal, Canada. Father went first and found a position at the Jewish hospital where anecdotally, all the non-Jewish physicians were Haitian. After two years of paving the way for us, my mother, my siblings, and I joined him in Montreal.

Growing up in Montreal, I was a good student, I had many friends, and I was a happy kid. My father always wanted to actualize his dream of sending at least one of his children to France for their formative years. When I was eleven, as the only girl with a strong personality (maybe a little too sassy for comfort), my father decided I was the one to send on a transatlantic airplane trip to Paris, France for secondary school. My mother was not allowed to travel with me, I would find my inner strength and resilience through this experience.

Mother Superior, principal of the all-girl boarding school, was waiting for me with my name on a whiteboard in Paris at the Orly airport. I entered the beautifully restored

17th century castle now convent in the suburbs of Paris near Porte-de-Vincennes. The interns would arrive on Sunday night and go home on Saturday at noon when classes ended. Wednesday afternoons were extracurricular afternoons and students from all over France would go to museums and experience art. I lived with twelve other girls in one of five one-room dormitories and we were supervised by a freshman/resident attendant from a nearby university. During weekends, the girls would go home, but I stayed behind with the nuns since my family was on the other side of the Atlantic. I would go to church with the devotees, help take care of the dogs, and read in my room. I was an easy-going happy child, but the days were long. The youngest of the nuns really liked me; she would spend a lot of time with me and would sleep in the big dorm with me so I would not feel lonely and scared sleeping in this vast space alone.

After a few weeks and weekends of being alone at the convent, Mother Superior became uncomfortable with the situation and started calling and asking her friends to invite me for the weekend at their houses. I remember every Saturday I had my little suitcase ready and a new French family, acquaintances of my principal, would host me for the weekend. After spending four or five weekends in a row with different people, I met a young couple with three children, two boys my age and their daughter who was about to turn one-year-old. It was love at first sight. I spent the weekend and it was as if I always knew them. They invited me over, weekend after weekend, until that summer when my parents invited them to come to Montreal. It was their first transatlantic trip, and after this visit our relationship grew, and they essentially became my second parents.

I continued my schooling in France for the next seven years until my father decided it was time for me to come home. He enrolled me in high school to finish my last year, and then I began my undergraduate studies in biology and exercise science at Concordia University in Montreal.

When I returned to Canada, somewhat against my will, I was looking for my identity, my raison d'être. At the age of 25, I flew back to Haiti for the first time on my own and enrolled in medical school. Studying medicine in French after doing my undergraduate studies in English was challenging and exhilarating. The rigorous training (very hands-on) which from the beginning of my first year included spending all afternoon in the hospital was a linguistic tour de force. Although I am of Haitian descent and proud of my heritage, I only spoke French. All my patients only spoke Creole, so I had to quickly adapt and relearn the language of my ancestors. My patients, all underserved peasants at the General Hospital in Port-au-Prince, became my personal Creole teachers. Today I'm proud I can speak authentic Creole taught to me by the real bearers of this beautiful and very musical language.

In 1991, I graduated at the top of my medical school class. A week after my graduation I married the chief resident in ophthalmology who just received a two-year paid fellowship to go to Paris VIII, Hospital Bichat and work on HIV and the eye. It was a wonderful new beginning for us. My adoptive French mom who had come to Haiti for our wedding insisted we stay at her mother's home since Grandma had just been diagnosed with Alzheimer's disease and moved to a specialized nursing home. While in France I had an opportunity to do a six-month internship on the medicine service at Hospital Tenon, Paris X, while simultaneously pursuing classes in public health. At the end of our first year, our first daughter was born, premature at 32 weeks, and I had to let go of my intention to finish my master's in public health.

After completion of the ophthalmology fellowship, our plan was to return to Haiti for my husband to open his practice in ophthalmology and for me to pursue my career in primary care. The political unrest in Haiti at the time made us rethink our intentions as it became challenging to consider raising our daughter in this unstable environment. We decided to pursue the American dream. We flew back to Montreal Canada to my family and studied for a year to sit and pass all USMLE exams as well as the exam of the Medical Council of Canada. My husband knew ophthalmology was not offered to foreign medical graduates. He made the logical decision to apply to residencies in primary care and we were grateful when he was offered an intern position at University of Miami (UM) /Jackson Memorial Hospital (JMH) in the Department of Family Medicine. Dr. Michel Dodard was the Residency Director and he quickly became my husband's mentor, friend, and almost a father figure. When I first arrived in Miami, keenly aware that our three-year-old daughter would struggle adjusting to having both parents in residency, I took a position as a medical assistant in a small Port of Miami clinic. The physician and owner of the practice accepted the strength of my foreign medical credentials, and allowed me to take care of patients under his guidance. When the time came to apply for a residency position, I applied only to the UM/JMH program in family medicine. I knew I had found my calling: taking care of the poor and the disenfranchised Creole and Spanish speaking patients at Jackson. I have the best memories of my residency.

Doing my residency in family medicine at the UM/JMH was a gift. As a specialty, family medicine provided me all I needed to care for my patients in a holistic manner. Whether in the hospital or out in the clinics, taking care of children, adolescents, pregnant women, or the elderly, I was trained with the rigors of the scientific model and the bio-psycho-social model of care. All my patients were individuals with unique health and social issues. I was trained by the best. Our family medicine inpatient service was supervised by four attending professors from very different backgrounds and personalities and they complemented one another: Drs. Catherine and George Willis, Dr. Behnam Djahed, and Dr. Thomas Harrington.

I also had the privilege to train with renowned clinicians, professors, and mentors in most of the specialties. With my flamboyant, friendly personality, I got to know most people in all corners of the JMH system very well: including the janitors, the staff, the lab technicians, the nurses and physicians. I finished my training as Chief Resident and gave birth to my youngest daughter. I started my full-time clinical faculty career at Jackson Memorial seeing patients full-time at Jefferson Reaves Senior Health Center in Overtown, Miami, the same outpatient clinic at which I trained.

After two years of perfecting my unsupervised clinical and management skills taking care of very complex patients, I continued as a junior faculty member at the UM Department of Family Medicine and Community Health. Meanwhile, at home, we became the adoptive family of a very bright, talented young girl who needed a nurturing and encouraging home to pursue her God-given trajectory. My then husband and I now had three daughters.

I became the Medical Director at the Center for Haitian Studies clinic in the Miami neighborhood, Little Haiti and continued teaching and precepting family medicine residents at the Jefferson Reaves Clinic. In Little Haiti, I was a community preceptor for UM third year medical students, teaching the principles of evidence-based medicine and cultural diversity, awareness, respect, and competence. Another six years passed when I was presented with an opportunity in adolescent medicine to work in my family medicine department. I embraced the unique opportunity to educate and assist many disenfranchised children, adolescents, and their parents, navigate the health system. I enjoyed collaborating and consulting via telemedicine with my university colleagues in different specialties.

Subsequently, I became the Clerkship Director for Family Medicine and teaching in the classroom became my next challenging task. I knew I was meant for the one on one patient-doctor or physician-student relationship and interaction but teaching in the classroom was a tall order. I was suffering from impostor syndrome; I did not know I would succeed. The chairman of my department, Dr. Robert Schwartz, must have seen something in me I did not see in myself. He convinced me to take the position for only three months after which, he promised, to move me if I was not satisfied. I have been humbled and honored with multiple George Paff teaching awards from my students. On many occasions, I was honored as their Student Marshall, to lead a graduating class at their commencement ceremony. I also became involved with the Admission's Committee and after a few years became the Assistant Dean for Admissions and Diversity. I believe that my presence and my enthusiasm has helped change the first impression of our medical school and that many more students of color are looking at UM as a possible and suitable place for their training.

Primary care, especially Family Medicine, is undervalued and not well respected in a specialty-driven enterprise like UM. The applicants, the medical students, the residents, and the patients are indeed my raison d'etre in this environment.

Often, I self reflect on my trajectory. I have been and continue to be a very good citizen for my institution. I am omnipresent as I am involved in all activities – volunteering in many of the school committees, from the Faculty Council to Women in Academic Medicine, and the many search committees for chairs and deans just to name a few. I have come to terms with the fact that participating in all of these activities will not translate into promotion in an academic setting. An academic rank is not something I want to be remembered for. Rather, I will be content if the younger generation of very diverse students and physicians count me in the group of teachers and mentors that helped them see the possibilities and forge their path. ■

JoNell Efantis Potter, PhD, APRN, FAAN

Professor of Clinical Obstetrics, Gynecology &
Reproductive Sciences
Vice Chair, Reproductive Sciences
Chief, Women's HIV Service
Director, THRIVE Clinic
University of Miami Miller School of Medicine

Currently, I am a clinical professor in the Department of Obstetrics, Gynecology and Reproductive Sciences and serve as vice chair of the department's Reproductive Sciences Section. My journey to this point in my career has been an arduous process, yet challenging, exciting, and personally and professionally fulfilling.

I grew up in an immigrant family in Miami. My grandparents came to the U.S. from Europe (Greece and Italy), and both of my parents are first-generation Americans. My dad was a proud World War II veteran. Our family owned a restaurant; and, after high school, I was expected to marry and work in the family business. Instead, I wanted to go to college; in part, so I would get a good job and not have to work in the restaurant. The restaurant business provided a wonderful lifestyle for my family, but it was just not what I wanted. What I did want to do was go to college and get a degree in nursing. I graduated with my nursing degree from Florida State University and was the first female in my family to attend college.

In the 1980s, my career began at UM Medical School and Jackson Memorial Hospital during a transformative period in Miami's history that brought changes to Miami's community and culture. A mass emigration of Cubans began after a surprise announcement by Cuban President Fidel Castro. Over 125,000 refugees arrived in Miami within a short time period. Around the same time, fifty to seventy thousand Haitians also were arriving by boat from Haiti escaping years of political chaos, food insecurity, poverty, and limited resources, arriving with only the clothes they were wearing. They were hungry, scared, and had tremendous health care needs. Simultaneously, another group, the infamous "Cocaine Cowboys," were bringing cocaine, organized crime, and the drug war to Miami. The city's infrastructure was overwhelmed, taxing law enforcement, schools, the labor market, and the public health system. In addition, we discovered South Florida had an emerging AIDS epidemic, and Jackson Memorial Hospital was the only hospital in South Florida willing to accept people living with HIV. As a nurse practicing at Jackson I learned about fear, abandonment, and stigma from the HIV patients. I also learned about the strength of the human spirit. It was during this experience, while caring for and listening to my patients tell their stories of sacrifice and resilience and watching their struggle to survive, I found my passion and purpose.

I was incredibly fortunate to have a great mentor. Dr. Mary Jo O'Sullivan, a physician and maternal-fetal medicine specialist who trained in the 1960s when women in medicine had to fight to get in and survive in a field dominated and controlled by men. She was a champion for equity and was a fierce advocate for the most vulnerable. And, she was tough as nails! She was my boss, and we were a team. I was responsible for the research enterprise, and she was the clinician scientist. Together we built a clinical research program that provided us with the opportunity to be involved in some of the most significant research impacting women's health over the past century. The research included the landmark 076 clinical trial, that demonstrated mother-to-child HIV transmission could be prevented; the Women's Health Initiative, the National Institutes of Health-sponsored clinical trial that studied the effects of hormones and diet on postmenopausal women; and the HPV vaccine trials for the prevention of cervical cancer.

Since my mentor was clinically so busy, I attended meetings for her. In her role as chief of obstetrics and vice chair for the department, many of those meetings were with high-level executives, prominent and successful researchers, and medical school senior leadership. Often, I was the only female in the room, except for perhaps the secretary taking minutes. As an assistant professor, I was the lowest ranking faculty member at the table. However, attending these meetings gave me the chance to develop skills that later influenced my professional career trajectory. I learned about leadership, board-room politics, and that listening was a powerful tool. I also learned how to offer thoughtful and impactful contributions to discussions and timing was everything. Learning about the people at the table, and how to address their egos, their strengths, and their weaknesses, was an effective strategy I developed to become heard, valued, and respected.

In these early days of the epidemic, faculty were focused on finding clinical therapeutics and interventions to stop the spread of AIDS and prevent new HIV infections. During strategic planning meetings, we discussed how to engage a culturally diverse, medically indigent population in Miami and provide state-of-the-art treatment, through rigorous investigational clinical trials. During these discussions, I thought about my patients, their struggles with hunger, housing, poverty, safety, and general despair. I decided to make an impact on their lives, I could focus on helping them access emerging therapies appropriately by designing comprehensive care and treatment models based on what they needed to survive and thrive.

Over time I gained my colleagues' respect and became valued and sought after to engage and participate in patient-centered planning activities. I had a front row seat at the planning table for engaging and collaborating although I was there by default, as the alternate for my boss and mentor. As the research teams discussed recruitment and retention, the models of care we designed provided access to target populations to be screened and enrolled. It also provided our patients access to innovative state-of-the-art clinical therapeutics and optimal health care.

This process set the stage for my 40-year career trajectory and I became a Ph.D. researcher in a clinical department at a major urban medical and research institution in Miami-Dade County. However, my path to professor and vice chair has not been without some bumps along the way.

Balancing work and family life with an active academic career are a struggle in any discipline or career. However, building a successful career, primarily in obstetrics and maternal fetal medicine, with physician scientists who work 24 hours a day, seven days a week, is extremely challenging for a person's personal and family life.

Long outpatient clinic days and births in the middle of the night, when specimen collection was critical, were daily occurrences. Having a spouse who understood the lifestyle and did not mind the 3:00 a.m. beeper calls, the missed dinners due to late clinics, and middle of the night rides to the medical center helped me survive the early years of my marriage. I was fortunate to find a spouse who understood the importance of my work and filled his time with his own interests. Living in Miami with its great sports and fishing helped – until we had children! With my first-born, I was busy establishing a national reputation and moving toward academic promotion from assistant to associate professor. My husband was happy to travel with me, and he and my daughter explored new cities and took naps in the hotel room. This allowed me to travel to national meetings for my career and not worry about my family back at home. With hard work and my family's support, I was successfully promoted. Although, when I had my second child after one or two attempts to travel with two children, my husband drew the line. If I needed to travel, I would be going alone. This was not something I wanted to do, so I had to make some profound career choices. In addition, my husband's new business took much of his time, and now he was having to spend long hours away from home. With not much family around for support, we choose to hire a live-in nanny. During my children's infancy and early childhood, having Olga as an extension of our family significantly improved my life-work balance and reduced chaos at home. She was able to care for the children, engage them in enriching play, and ensure they were safe and fed.

By this time, I was an associate professor and was engaged in important work. For my family, I decided I needed to modify my work environment. One thing I did was hire folks to take the night call and cover the clinics. Another was to stop attending meetings after 5:00 p.m. However, my decision significantly impacted my career; because my colleagues, physician scientists and busy clinicians, held their important meetings at night after clinic hours. Work was important and that professorship was certainly a goal, but my plan to be a full professor by age 50 would be delayed. In the meantime, I had quality time with my family in the evenings and on weekends and was at peace with my decision.

When the children started school, we reached another milestone in our family life. There were play dates, drop off, pick up, classroom activities, after school sports, field trips – with the expectation that parents, not the nanny, needed to engage and fully participate. We were always the first car in the school drop-off line and I would literally be pushing my children out the door as my beeper started blaring. I vividly remember my daughter's rants about why I could not be a "normal" mom and stay for flag and morning announcements like the other moms. There also were times when I would give them a bit of Tylenol at first signs of a sniffle, just to avoid keeping them at home. If I received a call from the school nurse, I would ask her to give them Tylenol, just to give me a few extra hours at work before I would have to pick them up. On one occasion our nanny had to fax my daughter's homework, so I could guide her over the phone while I was still at work.

Because I married the most compatible spouse, we discussed and decided on a plan to best meet our family's needs for work-life balance. Neither of our jobs were going to make us rich, but my job provided the stability of benefits, including health insurance.

Since our life goals were to live simply and enjoy our lives, we made the choice to scale back my husband's business. He became the after-school pick-up and drop-off guy and was present in the morning at the children's school flag-raising ceremony. He was the volunteer coach for after-school soccer, flag football, and basketball as well as the chaperone for field trips. He was the car-pool organizer and snack guy for swim practices and swim meets, and he became the family chef and homework helper.

I continued to keep my work-life balance rules, and only took speaking engagements in cities where my family could join me (lots of Orlando, Florida talks). I continued to skip the evening meetings until the children finished with high school, so we could enjoy family dinners every evening. My husband continued to maintain his business, and we agreed I would cover Monday and Thursday, if we needed to stay home with a sick child. To allow this, I never booked a clinic or meeting on those days that I could not cancel at a moment's notice. My husband made similar arrangements for the other three days.

Once the children were successfully entrenched in college life, I was able to spend more time on my academic portfolio. I accepted more speaking engagements and began to build my national and international reputation. It also was important to work towards my academic promotion and I participated in strategic medical school and university committees; and, through the relationships I fostered over the years, I was recognized and elected by my peers to join these committees and, at times, serve as chair.

In closing, I share my career path and personal choices and sacrifices my family and I made to allow me to balance my work in academic medicine with my family life. One's life course and goals are affected by many factors that sometimes may require a temporary detour, but success is possible. May all of you who took the time to read my story find some value. I wish you great success as you find your passion and your purpose, and hope you enjoy the journey along the way! ■

Teshamae Monteith, MD

Chief, Headache Division
Fellowship Program Director
Associate Professor of Clinical Neurology
Department of Neurology
University of Miami, Miller School of Medicine

My name is Teshamae Monteith, M.D. and I am an Associate Professor of Clinical Neurology, Chief of the Headache Division, and Program Director for the Headache Medicine fellowship at the University of Miami Miller School of Medicine. I am a double board-certified academic physician with a specialty in neurology and headache medicine. I serve on many advisory boards as a key opinion leader and I'm a clinical investigator for migraine therapeutics. I am a fellow of the American Academy of Neurology and the American Headache Society. I was awarded a National Institutes of Health (NINDS) supplement award to promote diversity in health-related research to study migraine and vascular risk factors, and complications such as silent brain infarcts, white matter lesions, and stroke as a part of the Northern Manhattan Study. I am one of the editorial board members for *Brain and Life Magazine* and a senior contributor for the *Neurology Podcast*, both produced by the American Academy of Neurology. I am fortunate to be successful, but my path was not always easy. I overcame my challenges with determination, a sense of humor, and a resounding belief in working hard for what you believe in. In times of hardship, I learned to tune in to that all-knowing voice within.

My mother was one of 12 children humbly raised in the countryside of Montego Bay, Jamaica. She was a quiet and disciplined child who prayed to be able to go to high school because at that time it was a luxury. Thankfully, she was one of two people to receive a scholarship to the University of West Indies. With that opportunity, she was able to escape poverty, train in Europe, and become a registered nurse. She married my father in New York, however, unfortunately he died when I was two years old. Despite raising three daughters as a single mom, I can't recall her ever telling us "you can't do that" or "no, no, sorry but that's not possible." She always had our backs and even the backs of our pets. I remember one summer while my sister and I visited Jamaica, my hamster Wilbur got out of the cage and disappeared. Although she did not like rodents one bit, she found Wilbur, picked him up, and returned him to the safety of his own cage.

We were highly energetic kids, filled with imaginations and a desire for discovery and independence. One day in elementary school, my sister and I decided to walk home on our own because we could not find our mom. We ended up waiting on the mat by the front door of our home because although we knew the journey home, we had not been given the keys. My mother and the school principal drove up with big sighs of relief and smiles on their faces. Our mother was gentle, accepted us, and often just let us be.

Growing up, I remained deeply connected to my paternal family. I enjoyed spending my summers with my grandmother in Jamaica, where she was an influential figure. Her passion for life and dedication to service was evident in all she did. She seemed to do everything well in her multiple roles as dressmaker, church deacon, florist, Senator, justice of the peace, and consumer rights advocate. However, she was widely known for her work as the founder and executive director of the Citizen's Advice Bureau and as a radio personality on a listener advice hotline. Her famous message was informative and reassuring and it was not uncommon for people to travel from across the country to our doorstep for more assistance. In witnessing my grandmother's work, I recognized very early that service to others was a natural extension of being human.

After graduating from high school in Miami, I attended Florida International University and majored in biology as a premed student. As a student I recall writing a personal statement as part of my application for the Honors College. I wrote about two African American males, one 19 and the other 21, that I had seen in the morgue. Both young men had multiple gunshot wounds all over their bodies. It was horrifying. Within moments, their fates were changed forever. I was accepted into the Honors College and did quite well in most of my courses but midway stumbled on a few academic challenges. After a period of self-scrutiny and growth, I found the right resources, and I was back in the flow. Decades later to my surprise, I was recognized as a FIU distinguished alumni and honored to be a recipient of the Torch Award. Life has many surprises, as a result of hard work but also chance.

I was lucky enough to get a position in a neuroscience lab through the Minority Biomedical Research Support Program, funded by the National Institutes of Health. It was through that opportunity that I presented my first abstract at a national conference for the Federation of Societies for Experimental Biology in Atlanta, Georgia. It turns out that my undergraduate training was a step that later led to volunteering at the Miami Project to Cure Paralysis under the direction of Dr. Allan Levi and a visiting neurosurgeon from France, Dr. Evelyne Emery. For me it was exciting just to be there with these incredibly accomplished, brilliant, and productive physician-scientists. I was so far away from my mentors, but knew I needed to get there.

I minimized my self-doubt, took the MCAT, and applied to medical school. I still can recall the sound of the mail truck approaching from blocks away as I waited eagerly for my supplemental applications. After many nights of studying, endless applications, and eventually several medical interviews, I waited to hear back. The wait was nerve-racking. I was both surprised but also assured, after I received the call from Dr. Robert Hinkley, the Dean of Admissions, who told me I was accepted into the UM Class of 2004.

Simply put, medical school education was tough, but it was also an exciting opportunity and at times felt unreal. One of the biggest challenges was the initiation into the culture of medicine; the diversity office for students was a helpful support center. Overall, I was privileged to be taught by dedicated and innovative physician-educators and honored to be trusted by patients during medical encounters. Medicine is both an art and a science. Overall, the demands were high, but the rewards were great and ultimately transformative.

When it came time to pick a specialty, I realized I wanted to understand the inner workings of the brain. I spent time with Dr. Walter Bradley (Wally), Chair of the neurology department, and helped to organize genetic and electrodiagnostic findings of patients with Amyotrophic Lateral Sclerosis (ALS) and their family members. I was somewhat intimidated by the devastating nature of this rapidly progressive neuromuscular disorder. I started to shy away from ALS research and chose to do an elective at New York University. I felt good being there partly because of the rigor of the clinical education and most importantly, I felt welcomed. During one of the clinics at the Veterans Affairs Hospital, I was shocked when one of the residents, Josh, blurted out to the residency program director, "Hey, Tesha wants to come here." I knew that I was being closely observed and tried to do my best. During my fourth year, I was thrilled to find out that I matched. Before moving to New York, I received spiritual counsel. I was advised to follow kindness and to listen intently to the recommendations of others with more experience.

I also matched for an intern year at Montefiore Hospital, a large university hospital affiliated with Albert Einstein College of Medicine in the Bronx, New York. For about one month I did not have a place to stay and thankfully was able to crash at my aunt's house about 15 minutes away, until my little studio dorm was available. I recall our first house staff mixer at the New York Botanical Garden. I gravitated towards another intern, Sean, who was equally apprehensive about what challenges our intern year would bring. However, I will never forget the reassuring words said that day by our program director, Dr. Sharon Silbiger, "It's going to be fine, fine, just fine." Mockingly, Sean and I would often pass each other on the wards, sometimes breaking into outbursts of laughter and repeat those famous words…it's going to be fine, fine, fine…. While things were inevitably fine, patients' disorders were medically complex. I also found it difficult to challenge teams regarding admissions (while rotating in the emergency room). However, I was also pleased when I followed up cases the next day and realized that I did the right thing. I only recently found out that Dr. Silbiger was the child of two holocaust survivors. In 2012, she lost her life to a long battle with chondrosarcoma. Although I don't know when she was officially diagnosed, I am grateful to her for teaching me to have courage and perspective in life.

Residency was an incredible opportunity to learn about the intricacies of the nervous system and the array of etiologies that can often lead to debilitating diseases. As residents, we had important responsibilities to care for patients in clinics and in hospitals. For the acutely aphasic plastic surgeon who teared up in my presence, the prisoner whose hunger strike was later complicated by central pontine demyelinosis, the newborn infant with spinal muscular atrophy, the intractable back pain of a patient with small cell carcinoma and aspiration pneumonia, the neuromyeleitis optica patient with vanishing fields of vision before my eyes, and later a colleague with an acute ischemic stroke, *I asked myself what more could be done?* There are many challenges inherent to resident education; it was very helpful to have a strong support system. I also took advantage of a great set of friends, the arts, visited great restaurants, and sometimes just took long walks around the city.

I found myself especially drawn to patients with headache disorders and wanted to learn more about the complexity of migraine. While in residency, I was introduced to advocacy. I came full circle, as initially I was rejected by the American Academy of Neurology's Palatucci Advocacy Forum (PALF) and then only a few years later named as the PALF co-advocate of the year in 2010. The truth is headache disorders remain underdiagnosed, undertreated, and highly stigmatized. Advocacy training was a way to learn how to use my passion to make change. I spent many long nights developing an advocacy initiative to develop research programs in chronic migraine and persistent post-traumatic headache in post-deployed soldiers returning from Iraq and Afghanistan. This soon became an obsession, as I became efficient at contacting members of Congress and meeting with staffers on Capitol Hill in Washington, D.C. I gained the support of colleagues, mentors, and persuasive society leaders. Advocacy remains an important part of what I do as a physician; I believe we are obligated to stay engaged for our patients and our profession.

After I completed my neurology residency, I did a fellowship in headache medicine at Thomas Jefferson University. Although I did not know until later, funding for my fellowship position was not secured. I was later told that Dr. Stephen Silberstein, my mentor, was going to pay for my salary out of his pocket in the event my position did not receive funding; however, the funds came through just in time. I did a second fellowship to pursue my research interest at the University of California, San Francisco; I was excited about the opportunity to work in a top program with two of the greats. I would be mentored under the direction of Peter Goadsby, MD, PhD, and participated in weekly round table sessions with Neil Raskin, MD. To think, I initially hesitated about taking the position. After a late workday while still in Philadelphia, I went to Au Bon Pain for a snack. The business was just about to close, and I was one of the only customers left in the store. I was stunned and almost jumped out of my skin as I walked through the door and over the loudspeaker heard the song...*I left My Heart in San Francisco* by Tony Bennett. I knew it was my destiny to go, and I felt like this was a sign, a very loud sign, as confirmation.

I was living in California; something I never could have imagined. Although the time was busy and the hours were long, there were many positive experiences. I loved discussing cases. I also soon started my own independent clinic after one of the physicians left the practice. When confronted, I reexamined my own medical perspectives. I also learned how to write a medical manuscript. I was proud to be part of a group that contributed to the scientific understanding of the origins of acute migraine attacks via PET imaging. Later the American Headache Society awarded our group the Harold G. Wolff Award for a study that would be published in *Brain*, as the *Premonitory Phase of Migraine – What Can We Learn from It?*

I returned to Miami to build the headache medicine program at the UM Miller School of Medicine. I love what I do as an academic physician. I am grateful for the mentorship, humbled by the courage of those that I treat, and remain in awe of the professional evolution of our trainees. Overall, this is a phenomenal time to practice medicine. There has been tremendous advances in some of the most difficult to treat and disabling conditions. For me, it has been a joy to share these advances as I educate other physicians across the country. I recall how nervous I was when for the first time I had to speak to almost 1000 physicians. My mentor knew I was nervous and reminded me this is supposed to be fun! I now visualize butterflies in my stomach as an indication of excitement and make it a point to look people in the eyes and share my enthusiasm.

There are several things you should do to maintain a satisfying professional and personal life as a clinician and researcher. Mentorship is critical to success, and while long distance mentoring has its challenges, technology makes it possible. In addition to mentorship, finding a sponsor is a way to have a career champion to advocate on your behalf. It is important to create a crystal-clear vision of what you want and to realize your desire can change over time. It is important to have a good fit with your institution and to know your value, your strengths, and your weaknesses. Allow yourself space for inspiration and envision what you want in the short-term and the long-term and prepare actionable plans to get there. Do not be afraid to ask questions and share your thoughts with others. It truly helps to create a network of support from within your institution, nationally, and if possible, internationally. In addition to traditional conferences, social media is a great place to connect. Lastly, it is incredibly important to take care of yourself. While work-life balance can sometimes sound like a myth; a predominately whole foods plant-based diet, regular exercise and sleep, social/spiritual support, stress management, and outside fun are important keys to the road to success. Most importantly, your larger life goals and mission should be aligned in all that you do. ∎

Epilogue by
Congresswoman Donna E. Shalala

As President of the University of Miami from 2001 to 2015, I am fortunate to have been involved in the growth of the school's academic medicine community. I came to UM after my eight-year tenure as Secretary of Health and Human Services in President Clinton's administration. By 2001, I'd spent most of the past decade thinking about medicine and health care, and as a woman in these male-dominated fields, I was determined to promote an atmosphere at UM in which women in medicine could succeed. It is a joy to read the testimonials in these pages and to know that so many female doctors and researchers have found a home on our campus.

These women have come to Miami from across the world—from the East Coast and West Coast, from Puerto Rico, Cuba, India, Venezeula, Colombia, Canada. They bring their unique backgrounds and experiences, passions and talents, to serve our shared community. Above all, that's what academic medicine is: a profession of service. It serves to excite students and to empower patients. It contains highs and lows—from the thrill of discovery to the long hours and daily sacrifices—but at the end of the day, academic medicine is about service. I know firsthand that living a life of service is the ultimate privilege.

Woven throughout these vignettes is the importance of mentorship, and in particular, of having women mentors. Women break barriers daily, and the stories in this collection attest to the strength and resilience of women to rise above historical limitations and skepticism from professors and colleagues. But it's easier to do so with a mentor who has faced the same professional adversity. I have enormous admiration for the ways in which each of these women has dedicated herself to giving back, to mentoring the next generation of women in academic medicine, to building an inclusive and diverse community.

As we bring more women into the practice of medicine, we can begin to undo decades of prejudices. The next generation of female doctors might still encounter sexist professors, departments where women feel invisible, and colleagues skeptical that a woman with a family can succeed in medicine. But with a strong community of women who've persevered, the women of tomorrow will be better prepared to overcome these challenges.

The lives of the women in academic medicine at UM demonstrate that it is possible to raise a family and break barriers in medicine. I'm grateful to know so many women who understand that having a family does not need to detract from their careers, but can instead make them stronger and more compassionate physicians. And it is heartwarming to read the reflections of their children who are inspired and empowered by their ambitious and successful mothers. I look forward to seeing some of these kids following in their mothers' footsteps and joining the ranks of the medical community at UM.

Diversity in medicine does not only benefit physicians. Studies have shown time and time again that diversity leads to better health outcomes for patients. When patients and doctors share an identity—whether race or ethnicity or socioeconomic background or gender or sexual orientation—patients feel more heard and receive better care. Women in medicine are making a difference not only through their talent as researchers and doctors but also by virtue of simply being who they are. As we work to reduce disparities in health care and outcomes, diversifying our medical workforce will play a critical role in this effort.

It's important for us to tell these stories because academic medicine does not exist in a vacuum. It is influenced by the world in which we live, in which some communities receive boundless resources and others are ignored. Over the past few decades, we've already taken strides to make medicine more egalitarian. We've expanded women's participation in clinical trials and increased funding for research in women's health, but this work is not finished. I hope that when women considering medical careers read these accounts of life in academic medicine, they understand the enormity of the impact they can make in their communities in the next few decades. I hope they know we're rooting for them. ■